ANYTHING IS POSSIBLE

MY KIDNEY TRANSPLANTATION STORY

KEN KIRWAN

MY HEALTHY, ACTIVE AND HAPPY LIFE SINCE TRANSPLANTATION

This book is dedicated to my family and my kidney donor.

ANYTHING IS POSSIBLE

MY KIDNEY TRANSPLANTATION STORY

INGRAM
CONTENT GROUP

Published by
Little Poppy Media
169 Steeplechase Green,
Ratoath,
Co. Meath,
A85 RC96

ISBN: 979-8-8858-9789-1

© Ken Kirwan

Cover image: Photography by Brian Rutter

Printed in the UK by
Ingram Content Group UK Ltd
Chapter House, Pitfield,
Kiln Farm,
Milton Keynes
MK11 3LW,
United Kingdom

Contents

Introduction

This book is my account of a journey I embarked on 21 years ago. It is a journey that has had many ups and downs, but I feel that the whole experience has made me a stronger man with endless positivity and a zest for life I never knew I possessed. I now look to each day as an opportunity to better my life and my family's life.

We all have our good days and bad days, but when you are diagnosed with any long lasting condition, you may experience more bad days than anything else.

In this book, I want to let people know, who may experience these feelings on a daily, weekly, or monthly basis, that these feelings can be replaced with good ones by doing the stuff you dreamt of but maybe never had the courage to do.

When you do these things, be they small or large, you will experience a different kind of euphoria, as they give you so much satisfaction and piece of mind.

I know it's easier said than done in a lot of cases, but if I can help a small amount of people achieve a better, more positive life by reading this book, I will be a very happy man.

Chapter 1

The early days

Most babies come into this world kicking and screaming, but I came in fighting for my life. I am the second youngest of my siblings. It's still a running joke to this day that I receive favouritism from my mam, Marie, because of my varied medical history. In fairness, as a joke I do play up to it when it is mentioned.

I was born with a very low platelet level called thrombocytopenia. It is a condition in which you have a low blood platelet count. Platelets (thrombocytes) are colourless blood cells that help blood clot. Platelets stop bleeding by clumping and forming plugs in blood vessel injuries. It is a quite serious and life-threatening condition.

I was kept in incubation for six to eight weeks which I am sure for my poor mam and dad must have been a very traumatic time, as when you have a new baby, you just want everything to be one hundred percent perfect.

As a father now myself, I have seen my oldest girl, Nicole, go through operations and ill health which breaks my heart, as you feel helpless, but thankfully, as I write this, my youngest daughter, Amelia, has not encountered any medical or hospital emergencies, fingers crossed.

My regular trips to the hospital or my medical problems did not stop there. I seemed to spend a lot of time in the hospital as a kid which was not ideal for my parents and I.

2

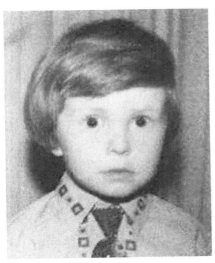

Me, aged 6 in my first school photo

Don't let the cute curls fool you, I was a ginger Dennis the Menace

One such incident took place at the age of five. My friend Liam said that his dad was going to bring us fishing, so off I skipped home, determined to retrieve a fishing rod we had buried in the corner of our garage, instead of calling my mam and dad to help me, in my stubbornness, I tried to wedge it out and it sprung back and the eye of the rod, went into my own eye. The pain was excruciating and I still remember to this day the panic that ensued. I could have easily lost the eye. That was another six weeks spent in the Eye and Ear hospital with a patch on my eye, which at the time I thought was quite cool. What did I know? I was five. I never had much of a love for fishing after that I can tell you.

Fast forward a few years later and the focus had shifted from my eye to my ear. I started having problems with my right ear, where it would discharge all the time with a liquid that had a horrible odour. I have spent my whole life with cotton wool in my right ear and still do to this day, as it was never sorted. Growing up it was quite embarrassing especially with members of the opposite sex.

After many an afternoon spent in the Eye and Ear hospital outpatients department, I had grommets put in a couple of times. Grommets are tubes surgically implanted in the eardrum to drain fluid from the middle ear. These procedures never worked, I can tell you that now.

Countless operations on my ear after that and nothing the Eye and Ear doctors ever did worked, and as a result I am two thirds deaf in my right ear which is quite ironic with my chosen second profession you will hear about later on in this book.

I vividly remember being in the Eye and Ear hospital one St Patrick's Day. I could hear the parade faintly in the background. I felt so lonely that day and cried until I sobbed, I was never a big lover of hospitals and still to this day I don't like them.

I think most people will vouch for this but when I was a little boy, I was a rascal. I will use that term, but I am very sure other people will use more derogatory terms. I was like a ginger Dennis the Menace. I think my mam spent most of my young life apologising and uttering the famous line, 'My Kenneth wouldn't do that'.

My earliest juvenile dalliance was getting expelled from kindergarten. Most of the world's biggest criminals cannot compete with me on that count.

My mam was asked to take me home, just for a few days, but she never brought me back. One of the children that I nearly scarred for life mentally is ironically one of my best friends to this day, Noel Murphy. God bless him after what I put him through.

I have definitely mellowed with age, becoming a father to my beautiful eldest daughter, Nicole, at 23 on the 18th April, 1998 and being diagnosed with poly-cystic kidneys at 25, forced me to grow up a lot.

Then in 2013, my second child, the beautiful and wonderful, Amelia Lily, was born on March 17th. Both my kids have turned me into a big softie.

Strangely enough, I never experienced any problems with my kidneys as a child, and my condition is also supposed to be hereditary but neither of my parents had kidney problems. When I enquired about this with my doctors in the last few years they explained it can happen once in a while, where it is just a freak, stand-alone incident or condition. I pray all the time that it doesn't be passed onto my children.

Chapter 2

Long, hot, great summers

I spent my childhood holidays in Skerries, a beautiful seaside coastal town where my mam and dad would rent a quaint, white house opposite a shop called Murray's shop. I have brought my own children there, over the years and I still get that nostalgic feel, everytime I drive through a certain arch way that leads you into Skerries town.

Across from Murray's shop there was a pub called The Black Raven. Very fond memories were had there. One such memory was when I watched the whole of *Live Aid* there, the great charity concert that was organised by Boomtown Rats singer, Bob Geldof and Ultravox lead singer, Midge Ure, to provide aid for the famine that was happening in Ethiopia. I think I was nine at the time. As a child I was crazy about music and I still am to this day. They were simpler times.

I watched the whole concert perched on a high stool with a packet of crisps, my mam and dad as well as my older siblings checking on me at regular intervals. All my fondest memories are growing up there, carefree, running around on the beaches, spending our days in the amusement arcade playing video games, and eating ice-cream.

My aunty used to own a mobile home in a caravan site

and my siblings and I struck up friendships with people our own age on the site. There was a huge group of us that hung around together and I am still in contact with a lot of them today. We were some bunch of scallywags, me probably being the worst of the lot.

The summertime always seemed to be much longer back then with endless days of sun and not an SPF factor cream in sight. That bold, mischievous streak that I possessed and still do was never too far away and my mam spent a lot of time apologising for my antics. I look back now as an adult and I am not proud of it.

Even the smell of chips with salt and vinegar today from a chipper reminds me of those days. We would spend the whole day at Toft's Casino & Amusements across from the South Strand and keep enough change for a white plastic tub of chips and a bottle of cola or lemonade on the way home. It was just Heaven.

They were fantastic times, times I will never forget. The main guys I hung around with were called Michael, Seamus and John. There were many others and many girls that I struck up amazing friendships with but we were all part of this great bunch of kids.

I remember one day in particular, Michael, Seamus and John all had a favourite video game in the amusement arcade called *'Galaga'*. We would play this until our hands were raw trying to get to the highest level we could. This particular morning, we realised after about an hour of playing the game, that the machine was broken and it was continually letting us play without paying for it. We literally took shifts going back to our respective parents to show our faces and have something to eat and drink but we never told them what was going on. We must have played that game straight for a full 13 hours before the people in the amusement arcade realised. What a day.

I had my first fishing trip down in Skerries also. I would spend a lot of time down by the harbour watching the boats and trawlers come in. It's still a beautiful place to this day and it's only up the road from where I live.

Top and bottom: Mam, my cousin zara, my cousin paul, my brother niall, me

From time to time we would take a big day trip to Mosney Holiday Centre, the Irish version of Butlins. All the parents and children would make the voyage for a fantastic day out.

While there, we loved to fill our faces with candy floss and sticks of candy rock. We would swim in the pool and go on all the various amusement rides which I think is why I can never go on any amusement ride as an adult. We all took a go on this ride called *The Tempest*. It seemed never-ending and I have never seen to this day that many people getting sick in unison after it. Looking back it was quite funny, at the time it definitely didn't feel that way.

I have spent quite a bit of time in Skerries in recent years, in a professional capacity. It will always have a fond place in my heart. I have brought both my girls at different stages in their life. It's a fantastic place for children and if you go up to Skerries on any given Sunday, this beautiful seaside town is packed with people.

At present, as I write this, we are planning a big reunion of all the kids from those days. I am very excited about this as it will be great to see them. Some of us are in contact on social media but to meet them in the flesh will be fantastic.

I may live out my years in Skerries by the sea or maybe Portugal, we shall see.

Chapter 3

I'm going to be a daddy

In 1998, at the age of 23, a year before my diagnosis, I became a daddy for the first time to a beautiful baby girl, Nicole Patricia Reilly, who weighed in a whopping 10 pound two ounces born at 1.15am, in Holles Street Hospital. I'll never forget it. I was changing jobs at the time and my leaving party was booked in a venue in town.

I was walking out the door when I received a call from Nicole's grandmother, 'You're not going anywhere, they are inducing today.'

It was all so real... it was happening. I'm not going to lie, I had mixed emotions. I could hardly mind myself, how was I going to be responsible for another person?

My daughter, Nicole and I, on her 16th birthday

I remember Nicole being wheeled out to me and just staring at her, not knowing what to say, I just kept whispering, 'I love you, 'I love you.' I was naturally worried about how life would change, would I be ok as a daddy? Many questions filled my mind.

I remember my best friend to this day, Brian Dromgoole, saying to me,

'Benny, it's time to sink or swim.' Benny is my nickname since the early 90s, I can't actually remember how the nickname came about to be honest but it stuck. What Brian meant was, I can continue on acting the goat and living my crazy life or I can try be the best daddy I can be. Thankfully I opted for the latter, but I still enjoyed my life when I wasn't being a daddy.

Every Friday, I would drive over to Dundrum after work with butterflies in my stomach at the prospect of seeing my little girl. I just loved watching her grow up.

Until I bought my house, we would stay in my mam's house. On the way home we would stop off for our sneaky McDonald's every Friday evening.

We would get up early every Saturday morning, watch all the kids' programmes on the TV, which to be honest, I really enjoyed. We would then get ready and head off for swimming. After swimming, we would usually head to the cinema and have our popcorn, drinks and mix the Maltesers with the popcorn. If it was a nice day after the cinema, we might head to the park. I knew I had to cherish these days, as they don't last forever.

Nicole is now 23 and a professional make-up artist, an art form in which she has shown amazing creative flair and built herself a nice, regular client base, running her own business. She will do very well in life and I am very proud of her. Like any father/daughter relationship we have had a lot of big ups and downs, but I love her dearly.

During these great days I speak of, my only interest was going out with my friends and enjoying myself as well as being a good daddy to Nicole. That was my first and foremost priority.

So off I went, being a young single man, I had a great time, probably too good of a time. There are certain people that will vouch for that.

Compared to today, back then I definitely did not take cake of my body the way I do now. Going to the gym was on and off and my diet was not nearly as strict as it is now. Sleep was a rare occurrence and over indulgence of alcohol and the wrong foods was in abundance.

In later years, I dreaded to think that my lax attitude to looking after myself may have contributed to my forecasted ailing health, but I was assured by doctors that it would have happened regardless.

About a year or so on after the birth of Nicole, I started to experience a dull pain in my side every so often, usually every four to five weeks which was proceeded by me passing pure blood in my urine. I had experienced it before, but it was now more regular.

Like most men out there I hid it, I didn't want to believe it was happening. I used to joke and say it was like a male menstrual cycle, as it happened every month, and I would be very cranky for a few days. Then it would go again and I would be relieved, until the next time.

After about three months, I swallowed my pride and I went back to the hospital to let them know what was going on and to find out exactly why it was happening. They did tests, tests and more tests, but they couldn't really find anything majorly wrong. Most times I got a prescription for painkillers to cope with the intense pain I was experiencing. It was just part and parcel of the process of what I was to find out.

It was a very embarrassing condition for me at the time as a simple thing like going to the toilet in someone else's house would be an epic task. You would have to be like a member of a CSI forensics team to make sure that you didn't leave any blood behind. Sometimes my lack of forensic cleaning knowledge let me down and I was forced to keep my poker face, if someone spotted blood on the toilet.

I remember when the owner of one house made a comment about blood being on the toilet surround. This actually happened at a party one night, and I just sat there and said nothing, as nobody knew what I was going through in detail with this gruelling health battle.

It also proved to be awkward at times with past girlfriends during that period, although I will spare you the finer details.

This cycle went on for the next few years, but it became a part of my life and I just learned to accept it. I never saw the bigger picture, as nothing was diagnosed or discussed at that early stage. I have always being a fairly positive person about life in general. I just got on with things.

Chapter 4

'Mr. Kirwan,
we need to have a chat...'

Emotions felt when diagnosed
with Polycystic Kidney Disease.

Fear and Anxiety

Denial

Anger

Feeling Down

How do I deal with all of this?

It's hard to know where to start, but here goes. I remember it as clear as day. It was a Thursday evening in my mam's house. I was 24 years old. It was a normal day, spent in work and when I came home, I had my dinner as per usual. I hadn't felt great all day with pains in my stomach area. I put it down to stomach cramps, but I also had an unusual dead pain in my lower back.

Every four to six weeks for the two years previous I was experiencing a dead pain in my lower back, but it always subsided after a few days.

As the evening drew on, the pain in my lower back got progressively worse and less than an hour later I was writhing around in unbearable pain on my mam's bed. It was then I decided to go to our local hospital, Beaumont Hospital in Dublin.

I was admitted and saw the triage nurse who, at that point, had no idea what it could be. She put it down to possibly being constipation, as I was having problems that evening in that department.

That evening, it was particularly busy in the hospital. The wait to see a doctor felt even longer than I could ever have imagined. Sitting there in excruciating pain, the minutes felt like hours. As the evening turned into night and then into the early hours of the morning, my calm demeanour began to fade. I really wanted to know what was wrong. I had been sitting there for at least 13 hours with no concrete diagnosis. In that length of time, the only conclusion they had come to was that it was very bad constipation. I had been given many painkillers, and what can only be described as dignity killing suppositories, but there was still nothing concrete in the way of a diagnosis.

A new doctor had just come on for his shift around 6am that morning and he decided after conversing with the team on call that I would be sent down for an X-ray on my lower abdomen and back, to try to determine what was going on.

In my weary, tired state, I went for the X-ray and came back and sat back down and had a little sleep on the most uncomfortable, back pain-inducing chairs. I was awoken by a very gentle and reassuring nurse who asked me to follow her to the doctor's office.

I will never forget those words when I entered the doctor's office.

'Take a seat there Mr Kirwan, we need to have a chat,' he said.

What he did next was quite strange, he took an A4 piece of paper and got a black marker from his desk. He drew two ovals on the piece of paper and then like a child, he stabbed the black marker with a succession of dots within the two ovals.

He handed me the piece of paper then, 'See that Mr. Kirwan? That's your kidneys.'

I was naturally shocked and stunned.
I was lost for words.
'What are they. What's wrong?' I spluttered.
Well Mr. Kirwan, you have what's called polycystic kidneys' the doctor declared.

A statement that rang through my ears for the following years. I didn't know what to say, I just wanted to know could it be fixed. Would I be ok? What did it all mean? The doctor's next statement was the strangest of them all.

'It's like being born with blue eyes, he said. 'Its not life threatening.'

How wrong that statement proved to be.

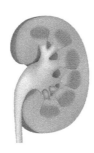

Polycystic kidney disease (PKD)

*Polycystic kidney disease (PKD) is an inherited disorder in which clusters of cysts develop primarily within your kidneys, causing your kidneys to enlarge and lose function over time. Cysts are noncancerous round sacs containing fluid. The cysts vary in size, and they can grow very large. Having many cysts or large cysts can damage your kidneys.

Symptoms

Polycystic kidney disease symptoms can include:
- High blood pressure
- Back or side pain
- Headache
- A feeling of fullness in your abdomen
- Increased size of your abdomen due to enlarged kidneys
- Blood in your urine
- Kidney stones
- Kidney failure
- Urinary tract or kidney infections

*https://www.mayoclinic.org/diseases-conditions/polycystic-kidney-disease/symptoms-causes/syc-20352820

Chapter 5

My first home and my first real taste
of polycystic kidney disease (PKD)

Fast forward to 2004, I had secured myself a fantastic job with Dell computers in their newly set up design studio. I'm a graphic designer by trade. It was a brilliant job and a great place to work where many friendships were formed and are still going strong today. A huge thanks has go to Tony Doyle, Emily Store and Mairead Murphy for giving me that fantastic opportunity.

It was a very well paid job, which afforded me more security financially than I ever had before. I went for years thinking I would never be able to buy my own home and all of a sudden that dream was starting to become a reality.

I started the arduous process of trying to get a mortgage with the help of my accountant at the time, Barry Walsh. After many months, hours of stress, many emails, and countless phone calls later I eventually got the news that I had been accepted for a mortgage.

This to me was a tremendous undertaking as I was buying the home on my own. I was determined to do it and low and behold 15 years later I am still there in the beautiful village of Ratoath in County Meath. Anyone that knows me, knows that I am far from. Mr. DIY, so when people walked into the house six weeks later for the house-warming, fully furnished with a 16ft decking outside, there were a few shocked faces believe me... none more so than my own!

As the months drew on, I loved having my own home but with that comes the household chores, and coming from a man that didn't leave the mammy's house till he was 30 years of age, I wasn't Mr. Domesticated. I was a mammy's boy through and through, but I struggled on.

Many afternoons coming home from work, I would have great intentions of hanging out the wash I put on that morning before I left. I would get home from work each evening, get myself sorted and make my dinner. I would then be hit with this wall of tiredness that meant I would have to lie down. More times then I care to remember I woke up on the couch at 10 or 11 o' clock at night after lying down for a 'quick nap' at 6pm that evening.

I knew there was something wrong, but as I wasn't very versed on kidney disease or kidney failure, I didn't realise what was happening to me. One of the main signs of early onset kidney disease is chronic fatigue that comes out of nowhere and hits like you like ton of bricks. I started to experience this in a big way.

I was also encountering a lack of concentration with everything. It would affect me in work where I couldn't understand why I was missing things. My job involved a lot of attention to detail. This led to many strained conversations with my managers, Lesley and Sherry. It was confusing to say the least, but I had no explanation for it. Thanks to both of them for sticking with me. On the other side of it, I was living the high life at the time. I had no money worries and was loving it. I kind of knew how sick I was, but nonetheless I would go out that night on a Saturday and most times I would end up staying out all night. I guess I was trying to block it out for as long as I could. I was fooling nobody but myself as the inevitable would eventually happen.

Looking back now, I knew well what was happening, but I was living in a world of denial where I didn't want anything getting the better of me. As far as I was concerned, I was not getting kidney disease. I just wasn't and that was the end of that, that was my foolish attitude.

I have always been a larger than life character. I am known for my outgoing personality and my larger than life way of going on and I didn't want to be seen as some kind of victim.

I had this lovely house, a lovely sports car sitting outside, a beautiful daughter, a great family and no money worries. From the outside, it looked like I was set up. And this blasted disease was not going to get the better of me ... How wrong I was!

Denial is a great place to be and a great emotion to hide behind, but only for a while, as sooner or later the symptoms get so bad that you cannot ignore them anymore. As much as I wanted it to not be the case, this disease WAS taking over me and my life. How I dealt with it then and life in general would become the blueprint for how I deal with it for the rest of my life.

Looking forward to the journey ahead with optimism

This road ahead is not going to be an easy one, but it's a far better one than the one I was on.

So let's buck up and face it head on with all the strength and positivity I can muster...

Still today that's the attitude I wake up with.

The only adversary you are facing... is you!!!!

Chapter 6
Music was my first love

From a young age, I always had a great love for music, listening to it; but not performing it. I was known to put on my dad's earphones and sit and listen to his albums at home for hours, I also used to religiously watch music TV programmes, such as MT USA that aired every Sunday, presented by the late Vincent Hanley. I loved that programme and it intensified my passion for music. In particular, I was a huge fan of Michael Jackson and my first album was his best-selling album, *Thriller*.

As the years went by, I realised I could sing and from the age of 17, I started to enter talent competitions with quite a bit of success. When I hit my 20s, singing and performing then took a back seat for no reason, other than I was enjoying life with my friends.

From listening to my dad's albums, I also grew to love another genre of music, that is swing and big band music. Music is something that has always kept me going through good and bad times, including my health journey. My dream of performing on the big stage was first realised in 2005.

A former friend of mine who owned The Irish Rat Pack swing band had asked me to design an album cover for him, for a charity he was supporting at the time. He had an upcoming concert in the world renowned Vicar Street venue in Dublin City Centre. I told him that I would design the album cover and sleeve in return for a guest spot on his show. At first he was sketchy and then we agreed on two songs on the night. I couldn't believe it. I started rehearsing the two songs every day, many times a day, to make sure I knew them back to front, off by heart.

After a few weeks, the day arrived. I never felt nerves like I did that day and night before going on stage to a crowd of 1,200 people.

My friend then and still to this day, Luke Thomas of The Swing Cats band, calmed me on the night with the help of Jack Daniel's and reassuring words.

The time came that evening, when my name was just about to get called on stage and I nearly ran back upstairs to the green room to hide.
'Ladies and gentlemen, Mr. Ken Kirwan!'

I walked out on stage. I use the term 'walked' loosely, as I felt like a new calf that had just been born and was learning to walk. My legs were like jelly.
The crowd was cheering and the bright lights were almost blinding. It was everything I had dreamed of, and more and more, it reignited a huge drive in me to pursue a career in performing and entertaining, which had always been a huge passion of mine.

The very special thing that night was my mam, dad, family and friends were in the audience to see me perform. My father, Noel was a huge Sinatra and Rat Pack fan. He loved all the swing artists of that era and was constantly playing the albums in the house.

'Son, listen to this, that is real music... timeless,' he would say.

I did as I was told.

My dad in his tuxedo, off to a black tie wedding with my mam

The two songs I performed on the night were 'Summer Wind' by Frank Sinatra and 'What a Wonderful World' by Louis Armstrong. Two absolutely beautiful standards by two of the greats of our time. The songs and my performance were met with rapturous applause. Thank God! I was still racked with nerves but the audience's reaction helped a lot.

As stories go, my dad had a tear in his eye that night but he would probably say it was just dust from the theatre. What I would give for him to be standing there watching me today.

I also played Vicar Street in 2007 with the Irish Rat Pack again. Sadly my dad was missing from the crowd and there was many a tear in my eye this time. But I know he was watching me from above and I feel he has watched over the whole family since he passed.

My dad had suddenly and sadly passed away on Oct 4th, the previous year, in 2006. This hit the family very hard and my mam who had known my dad 50 years of her life.

These performance opened up new doors for me, and I started getting calls and emails about guest spots and offers to join bands. It was a bit overwhelming at the start and I stepped away from it for a while out of sheer fear. I had taken a few future bookings in, but if I am being honest, I hadn't a clue what I was doing. I just knew how to sing. I knew nothing about the industry itself. It was all very new to me. It was exciting yet nerve wracking at the same time.

One of the bookings I had taken previously after the first performance in Vicar Street in 2005 was for my friend, Alan Fitzsimons of former global chart topping boy band OTT fame. he was marrying his beautiful wife, Siobhan the following month, November 2006.

Little did I know how hard that wedding was going to be for me personally which you will read about later on. But like a true professional the show went on, and I performed at the wedding.

From that day onward, it was always on my mind that I someday I would have my own headline show in a large theatre. I was determined to make that day happen.

Chapter 7

He did it his way

The year 2006 was one that I will never forget for many reasons. dad, Noel, was not in great health this year. He had collapsed a few times doing normal household and garden chores.

As I was living in my own home, I did not witness this. Things seemed ok. Me and my family put it down to age and my dad's own stubbornness. That blissfully ignorant streak in relation to my own health came straight from him.

My dad is his An Garda Síochána uniform, in his early twenties

In his younger days, my dad was a member of An Garda Síochána for over 40 years. He was a decorated and respected detective. He was a larger than life character. A very intelligent, well-read man. He was an avid reader; all fact, no fiction. It had to be when my dad was reading. Funnily enough, I am the very same today with my choice of reading.

I inherited a lot of traits from my dad. My lack of patience, my short fuse, my love of bad dad jokes, and of course, my passion for singing, amongst other things that I am sure my family and wife can attest to, but just not to my face. People say I look him too and my singing voice is very like his. We are very alike and sometimes I scare myself when I say or do something that is so similar to what he would have done.

In October, 2006, I took a trip to Leeds with a few friends for a lads' weekend. Now, I am sure you can imagine we were not drinking tea and eating digestives all weekend. I probably should have been taking better care of myself. Hindsight is a great thing looking back.

We flew out from Dublin on the Friday afternoon and from the time we hit the runway in Leeds airport, it was full steam ahead with the general skulduggery expected of a group of lads on holiday. It was a very enjoyable weekend but as my energy levels were at an all time low, and weekend was enough to nearly finish me off.

We flew back home on the Sunday and as always, I left my car at my mam's house. Our family home is a five minute drive from Dublin Airport.

I arrived at my mam's on the Sunday, weary and dishevelled. There was a strange atmosphere in the house. My dad was sitting in the front room watching TV, which was nothing strange.

My mam pulled me aside and said, 'Your dad collapsed again, but it was bad one this time.'

My brother Niall had arrived at this stage. My mam wanted to call an ambulance, but in true Dad style, 'I'm not getting in an ambulance, I don't want an ambulance!,

We finally got him to agree that we would drive him to A&E in Beaumont Hospital. Little did I know then that Beaumont Hospital would become my second home. We got in and got dad a wheelchair as he was quite unsteady on his feet.

What happened next and in the proceeding hours will stay with me for the rest of my life. We went into the triage nurse to get my dad assessed. My brother was parking the car. The nurse began to ask him simple questions like his name and address to which he had problems answering. I couldn't understand this at all and I even joked with my dad to stop messing around, and I ended up having to answer for him.

Now, take into consideration that my dad was a very proud, intelligent, articulate man. Due to a lack of medical knowledge on the part of my brother and I, we didn't realise that my dad was after having a mini-stroke, hence the difficulties he had in answering simple everyday questions.

The ironic thing is that we went back to A&E to wait for him to be called and he picked up a newspaper and completed a full crossword. It was like only a certain part of his brain had shut off. The last words my dad uttered to me on this Earth were, 'Ken, what is the first name of the lead singer with the band PULP?'. Look, it's six down on the crossword.

That was typical Dad, always doing a crossword or something to exercise his great brain.

The worse was yet to come. My two sisters, Yvonne and Triona, had arrived and after a few hours of waiting it was decided that I would go home to freshen up, get a few hours of rest, and go back down.

I had also started to get really bad headaches at that time, but like most men, I dropped a few paracetamol with the 'I'll be grand' attitude. However, these were not normal headaches. The pain was excruciating and they would hit from out of nowhere and take you down. I have never suffered from migraines. I am guessing that is what it feels like. The stress levels that I was experiencing with everything that was going on was driving my blood pressure sky high. Little did I know at the time that high blood pressure is a huge part of kidney disease.

My health was beginning to deteriorate very badly that year, but as always, I was running away from how sick I was. The fatigue I was experiencing was unbearable at times and even my skin pallor changed dramatically to a slightly grey hue. Of course, I was still living in complete denial, actually believing that this disease would just go away.

That night while I was at home I received a call from Triona to say that our dad had taken a turn. However, she said there was no point in rushing back down, that they would call me if there were any developments.

I woke up the next morning and had a bad feeling in my heart. I regarded this as pretty normal seeing as I was so worried about my dad. I rang my siblings and my mam and they said to go to work as there were no developments. I was only in work about an hour when I got a call to come to the hospital. I knew something was seriously wrong, but they didn't tell me over the phone.

As I arrived to the hospital I was met by brother Niall, who through tears and gritted teeth said, 'Ken, Dad has had a double stroke, it's not good.'

I broke down crying in my brother's arms. That moment to date is the worst of my life. I didn't know what to do, what to think. All my life, even though I probably gave my parents the most trouble out of all my siblings, cheek, hassle, embarrassment and more in abundance,

I never once thought that I would lose either of my parents so early in their lives or my life for that matter. My dad was only 71 when this happened.

That following week, we took it in turns to sleep in shifts in Beaumont Hospital. We didn't want to leave my dad on his own in the hospital. Even though he was in a coma, we know he was aware that we were there as they say people can still hear when they are in a coma. We spent most daytimes that week at his bedside reminiscing about old times and playing the music my dad loved. It was quite nice to be able to do that.

My mam never left the hospital the whole week. They had known each other nearly 50 years and she wasn't going to leave his side at all. We eventually convinced my mam to go home and have a proper rest in her own bed and come back the next day fresh.

My dad's love for my mam was true even in his last moments when he waited until she went home to slip away quietly with my brother, Niall, by his side. He took his last breath on the morning of October 4th, 2006.

He was finally gone to the big stage in the sky.

The medical staff that were looking after my dad were genuinely sad when the inevitable happened, as they went through every emotion like ourselves in that week that my dad lay in a coma. It seemed much longer than a week and the staff got to know us got to know us very well and vice versa.

My dad's funeral was a like that of a celebrity's. I have never seen Whitehall Church, our local church, as full as that day. It was a testament to the man that my dad was. His personality, jovial nature and presence made people warm to him, both in his profession, our local community and with friends and family. He always had a joke and laugh for everyone he met and was very forthcoming with help in our local community. He was a character in many ways and everyone that knew him, were the better for knowing him.

He had done it His Way.

Chapter 8

The 'D' word

2007 was the year that my life had changed in more ways than one. It was a year of great excitement as two of my best friends were getting married. I am grateful to be part of a close knit group of friends for the last 25 years. Two of the lads were getting married to their partners. They were were the first two of the group to walk down the aisle.

I was happily going out with a girl at the time and all was good, but I could feel my health worsening by the day. My energy was completely sapped, but as always, I thought I was invincible.

The blood in my urine was at its worst. The headaches were getting a lot worse and a lot more regular. I was taking paracetamol for the headaches like it was going out of business. It masked the pain a little but not completely.

My meetings with my doctor, Dr Peter Conlon, were getting more frequent too, as he knew what was happening. I'm sure he had seen it a thousand times before.

When I first met my doctor Dr. Peter Conlon, I didn't like him. He would always tell you the bad news, the stuff I didn't want to hear when I was trying to stay blissfully ignorant to what was actually going on with my body. I used to call him 'DOCTOR DEATH'. It was my irreverent attitude that was the problem. He is a very intelligent, well-qualified man who was trying to prepare me for the road ahead. I know that now.

We had briefly spoken about the 'D' word – Dialysis.

Dialysis is a process for removing waste and excess water from the blood and is used primarily as an artificial replacement for lost kidney function in people with kidney disease. I still considered dialysis as being a long time down the road for me. It was a lot closer than I thought.

Both the lads, stag weekends came and went and they were brilliant. I don't need to go into detail as to what went on, but we enjoyed ourselves... a lot. The weddings were both coming up in June and July of that year respectively. We were all very much looking forward to these days out.

The first of the lads to get married, Gary, was married in June and we had a lovely day and night. It was my girlfriend's first time to meet everyone, so I was nervous about that. It proved to be a fantastic day. The only bad thing about the day was my headaches were getting crippling at this stage and I foolishly took a full packet of paracetamol that day to try to get rid of the pain.

A month later it was my other pal's turn to walk down the aisle. Again, an amazing day. It was a two day affair, but I couldn't handle it. I hadn't told anyone how bad the headaches were and at this wedding they were no better. The headaches had doubled in intensity.

My girlfriend and I came home the next afternoon after the night before, naturally tired, but anyone that knows me, knows the most I sleep is about six hours a night. I am like a jitterbug and have a very active mind. That day in particular, we went to bed when we got home and I slept for 16 hours straight. I had never or have never to this day ever slept like that. When I woke up from that marathon sleep, my head throbbed. I didn't feel good at all. I actually thought I was having a stroke. After my dad having had a double stroke, this filled me with dread. That was a Sunday going into Monday. I will always remember it, it was hard to forget.

I finally swallowed my pride on the Monday and rang the hospital to make an appointment to see Dr Conlon. I drove down to the hospital on the Tuesday and went into the clinic as I had done many a times, except this time was different. I knew I wasn't going home with a prescription for painkillers.

I sat in Dr Conlon's office after getting my blood pressure taken and some other routine tests. He was never one for mincing his words or dressing anything up. He came straight out with it, 'Your blood pressure is sky high, that's why the headaches are happening. The time has come, you will be starting dialysis in a weeks time.'

The day of reckoning had come, it was a day I never wanted to arrive, and in my head I would keep telling

48

myself that is wasn't going to happen because I knew that once that day came, my disease was real. I didn't want to face this reality. I remember being asked about options of home dialysis or hemodialysis. It meant getting set up at home with a dialysis machine or coming to the hospital three nights a week for four hour stints. Hemodialysis is a treatment for kidney failure that uses a machine to send the patient's blood through a filter, called a dialyzer, outside the body. I chose the option of hemodialysis. The way I looked at it was once I did it in the hospital, I didn't have a constant reminder of it at home.

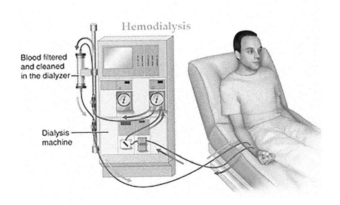

The doctors and nurses informed me I that would have to get a line in my neck or fistula in my arm, otherwise known as a vascular access. A fistula is a surgically created vein used to remove and return blood during hemodialysis. An arteriovenous (AV) fistula is a connection, made by a vascular surgeon, of an artery to a vein. It provides good blood flow for dialysis. These were needed for the needle access for dialysis. I was told this would be happening within a day or two. Up until now, the most thought-inducing choice I had to make in my life was whether to opt for a white shirt or a blue one. This was the way my life was changing, and it was all happening too quickly.

I didn't sleep a wink that night. There was a lot to process. It had been explained to me, but it was all happening too fast and to be honest, it was a bit of a blur.

I was back in work in Dell the following day as I had to let work know what was going on. My girlfriend had bought me a portable DVD player in the meantime. As I was saying before we were a very close knit group, three of my pals in work, Nick, Graham and Aidan, were avid DVD watchers and had loads of them at home. They said they would supply me with them for my dialysis nights in Beaumont Hospital.

The next step was to get the fistula operation which I was dreading as it would be done under local anaesthetic. I would rather be knocked out for any medical procedure. This time that wasn't to be. It was done and dusted within an hour or two, but it was a strange feeling being awake during it. My upper body was behind a screen while they cut my arm open to do the procedure.

I was faced with another 'sink or swim' choice in my life. I promised myself that day that I wasn't going to let this define me or get on top of me. It is very easy to slip into a state of depression at the prospect of being on dialysis indefinitely, the dreaded wait to get onto the transplant list, and the whirlwind of emotions that comes with this life changing situation that people with organ failure are faced with. I basically said to myself that I would try to keep life as normal as possible.

I had to keep life relatively normal for Nicole, my daughter. Even though she didn't live with me full-time, I didn't want her to know exactly what was happening. She was young and I wanted to enjoy my daddy time with her at the weekends when I had her. I also didn't want to worry my mam or my family either, more than they needed to.

The schedule for dialysis, would be three nights a week in Beaumont Hospital, four hours a night until, one, I was put on the transplant list and two, they found a match for me for transplantation.

It was daunting to say the least, but I decided to take the bull by the horns and I convinced myself that it would be somewhere I had to go three times a week. I kept up a light gym routine and tried to stay in good enough health, just in case a kidney was found after I had been put on the transplant list. I also moved back to my mam's house, the family home in Santry, while I was doing my treatment. It's right next to Beaumont Hospital and it made better sense. I rented my own home out until everything was sorted, however long that was going to be.

Eventually, the inevitable night came when I had my first dialysis session. I was so scared about what to expect, plus, I am really bad with needles, but the nurses on duty were amazing, and they made me feel so at ease.

I did my first sessions in St. Damien's ward upstairs in the hospital, before I was to be moved to the dialysis unit. It was quite sore to start when you were getting set up. The nurses had to hook you up to the dialysis machine with two needles into seperate veins. That was quite uncomfortable at times, but once you were set up, you were always given your nice cup of tea and a sandwich. That simple meal of a cup of tea and a sandwich became the holy grail each night.

When you are experiencing kidney failure and you are doing dialysis you are put on a pretty restrictive renal diet, especially liquids, as your kidneys aren't working by themselves. My kidneys still worked but had very little function, so my liquid intake was whittled down to 1.5 litres a day. I had to factor in that cup of tea during dialysis sessions. There were many restrictions on the renal diet, and if you were a lover of salt, carbohydrates, stodgy food like chips, etc. it was going to be quite a hard journey.

Luckily, I had a decent enough diet at this stage and cutting these things out didn't really bother me.

The dialysis treatment started well I must say and I got used to it relatively quickly. The one thing I still couldn't curb was my party lifestyle, even though I was keeping a healthy enough lifestyle with the gym. I was still living in denial, a little so I rebelled at the weekends, drinking for the first few weeks meaning my liquid intake was well over what it should have been. Plus, it was also the wrong kind of liquid I was drinking! I usually did dialysis on a Sunday evening as my last session of the week, so when they asked me how many litres of fluid to take off me, I would say the maximum which was five litres.

This was really irresponsible of me, but it shows how much of an effect it can have on your life and how much you refuse to admit that it is happening to you. You still want to bolster some power over the situation. I eventually copped on and realised that I was only fooling myself and nobody else. I had gotten it out of my system literally, and it was time to knuckle down.

The one thing I did right through the treatment, as a show of defiance, was that I drove to and from treatment even though there was a free taxi service with a company called Blue Cabs.

After about eight or more weeks on dialysis, I had my evaluation with a lovely doctor and the director of transplantation called David Hickey, who had actually played for the Dublin GAA senior football team in 1974 and 1976. He was going to go through everything with me as it pertained to my eligibility for the transplant list.

By this stage, I was really looking after myself and had curbed my party lifestyle. I had also done all of the tests needed for eligibility. It was down to the gods now. I walked into his office and before I even sat down he said, 'You will have a kidney within a year!',

I was a bit taken aback by this comment and found it a bit unfair. Sometimes you can be on dialysis for 10 or more years if a kidney doesn't become available. Such a sentence can garner immense hope in someone who is desperate to get off dialysis, but to have that hope and for it not to come to fruition, it can be crushing.

I asked him to explain himself.

'I can tell by the colour of the whites of your eyes, your complexion and your physique that you are looking after yourself very well,' he said.

He also said, 'We want to put a kidney into a body that is healthy and a good healthy environment.'

Now, there are a lot more factors for a suitable kidney, mainly your blood group. I have a rare blood group and

I thought this would hinder, me but he assured me that it was an advantage, as there wouldn't be so many people in my transplant pool. It made perfect sense.

I walked away from that evaluation with a positive attitude. I was looking after myself very well, but I took his comment with a pinch of salt as I said to myself he wasn't a clairvoyant and couldn't make those predictions. How very wrong I was!

I got into a routine with my treatment where they would hook me up when I arrived, I would have the famous sandwich and cup of tea and then I would start watching my DVDs. Usually for the last hour of the four hour stint I would have a little sleep, as it would take a lot out of you and that was the routine three nights a week.

The nurses and healthcare assistants in the dialysis unit or any of the rooms that I received treatment were absolutely amazing people. I used to love chatting to them. They were such a positive and integral part of my treatment and kept me upbeat throughout the entire process. So, I want thank you all from the bottom of my heart... and kidney.

On and on I went with this weekly cycle of treatment, just taking it in my stride. At times I would secretly feel down, but I never let it show. I think somewhere in my heart I felt that I would get a kidney sooner than I

55

thought, and that is one thing that got me through that difficult time, a Positive Mental Attitude.

I had booked to go on holiday that year with my girlfriend to Lanzarote, and I had to get it cleared by the hospital, as I would still have to have my treatment while I was away. After a lot of to-ing and fro-ing, I was to do the dialysis session in Feurteventura, which was a boat ride away. It all had to be pre-arranged with the clinic, but they were amazing and everything was planned down to the finest detail. I only had to do one session though, thankfully.

The morning it was arranged was an excursion to say the least. We had to get up at 4am to catch a bus to the port to get a boat over to Feurteventura, which as I remember was an hour or so away, plus the four hour dialysis session and the same back. Needless to say, we were not able for much when we got back. Being honest, it was a bit surreal having to do it while on holiday but like everything else, you got used to it.

I have to praise my former girlfriend back then for her patience. She took part in the trip without a grumble or a grimace. She was with me through a lot of the process and I will never forget her kindness, patience and caring attitude.

The staff in the beautiful Feurteventura clinic were amazing and made me feel very comfortable. Thank you to all of you in the clinic as well.

As the Frank Sinatra song goes 'The best was yet to come and babe, won't it be fine?'

Positive Outlook and Life Goals

Positive Mental Attitude has got me through the worst times in my life, especially my sickness, my dialysis, and the loss of my dad.

The secret is to concentrate on the good things in your life rather than the bad. I still live by that today.

I purposely stay away from things or situations that bring negativity into my life as it only brings you down.

Live life and be happy, you only get one go at this...

Chapter 9

The best Christmas present
I ever received

It was December, 2007, and anyone that knows me, knows I'm a huge Christmas fan. By this stage I had gotten back into singing in a big way and I had been asked to do the Christmas shows in Fitzpatrick Castle Hotel with The Irish Rat Pack, which I was delighted and nervous about in equal measure. I continued my treatment through December with no problems. It had become second nature at this point, only this particular year I had been booked in for treatment on Christmas Eve, which was weird. I didn't mind, it had to be done, but it felt strange nonetheless.

We spent Christmas as always in my mam's house for dinner, which is always a big affair. Dinner with all the trimmings. For years our house was always and still is the house that all the neighbours come over to on Christmas Day. My dad was sorely missed and still is, around Christmas time as himself and my mam would always be the hosts on Christmas Day.

This Christmas, in particular, was extra special for me as it was the first time I was allowed to have my oldest daughter, Nicole, for dinner on Christmas Day. She was flying out to Spain on St Stephen's Day with her mam. I was delighted with that and we had a great day and night.

The Christmas shows had run right through December, every Friday and Saturday night and I loved being up on the stage in front of 300 to 400 people each night. To accommodate me being able to do the shows with no complications, I had to work my treatment around the schedule and I used to do my treatment at 4.00am on the Saturday morning.

The routine was gruelling looking back. I'd do the show out in Fitzpatrick Castle Hotel, get into the car at 12.00am, drive roughly an hour home to my mam's house, get into bed at 1.00am, sleep for two and a half hours and then get up and drive down to Beaumont Hospital to do my treatment. Those nights were extremely tiring and took a lot out of me, but as I said, it had to be done and that was that. My attitude was always and still is, 'I can do this... anything is possible'.

My coping mechanism for dealing with this disease and trying to stay positive was performing on stage, fitness and spending time with my family, as they brought me joy. I know this wouldn't work for everyone, but if I can give a small bit of advice to anyone going through something similar to what I was going through, it is to find what brings you joy and makes you happy, and pursue these things more if you can.

The morning of December 29th, 2007, at 3.30am, proved to be very different to all the others. I arrived for my treatment, was given my bed, and one of the nurses set me up as per usual. I was too tired to watch any DVDs so I just laid there and snoozed. I was falling in and out of sleep when my phone rang... PRIVATE NUMBER.

Now, on the whole I wouldn't be a great man for answering private numbers and I think because I was so tired that night, I didn't for one minute think it would be anybody ringing to tell me anything of importance, so I didn't answer it the first time when it rang. But, how wrong I was.

We were always told by the transplant unit to answer the phone no matter what time it was, in case they find a kidney for you because if they can't contact you, the kidney goes to the next suitable person on the list.

After the phone rang, the caller left a message and when I listened back, I couldn't believe what I was hearing. It was a lady called Regina from the transplant unit telling me that they had a kidney for me and if I didn't answer the phone, it would be gone.

I was getting a kidney!

What I didn't know was in the mean-time the guards had arrived at my mam's house in Santry, lights flashing asking where I was. Let's not forget that this is the middle of the night. My poor mam nearly had a heart attack, not literally. I frantically rang the number left by Regina on my message minder and got through to her. I did receive a few choice words from her which I totally deserved.

I was in deep shock and silent elation at the same time. I was getting a kidney transplant after only seven months of dialysis. Was this a dream? Was this really happening? Why was I so lucky? Obviously, they would have to do tests to see if the new kidney would be suitable, but it was estimated at a 90% chance of success.

I remember texting my family and everybody I knew to tell them, also Nicole was in Spain, so I made sure to contact her mam to let her know.

I also remember the nurses and the healthcare assistants in the dialysis unit rushing around the bed with big smiles at the prospect of me getting a new kidney. They couldn't understand why I wasn't shouting this from the rooftops, but again remembering, firstly, it was the middle of the night and secondly, a lot of the people in the dialysis unit are on treatment for a long time, some even 10 years, so it didn't feel right to be showing my true excitement there and then.

Inside, I was absolutely over the moon and could not believe that I was so lucky to have been blessed with this fantastic gift of life but also realising that someone actually died, carried a donor card and donated their organs. It is because of the amazing people that carry donor cards that people like me have a second shot at life, and I will always be truly thankful and indebted to my anonymous donor for the rest of my life.

My phone was hopping with messages of well wishes from everybody and wishing me the best of luck for the next few hours that would be spent getting me prepped for the big operation that was ahead. As I was saying, there were preparatory tests to be done prior to the operation to make sure all was in order and that it would be a perfect match.

My mam arrived at around 8.00am with pyjamas and toiletries along with anything else I needed because we knew I wouldn't be going home.

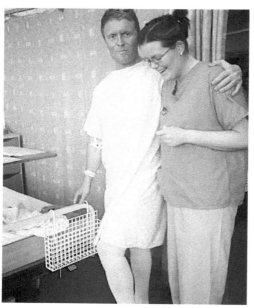

It was a surreal experience. The realisation hit that if it all went according to plan with the transplant and everything was okay, that I would be dialysis free within 24 to 48 hours. I thought I was still dreaming.

In my gown and compression tights, getting prepped for surgery

The early morning turned into the afternoon and I was still getting tests done such as blood pressure checks. I was in great form for a man that was going to be in a theatre in less than a few hours to undergo a huge operation. I was having the craic with the nurses. It was all quite a blur to honest but a nice blur. All my tests went fine and the doctor and his team were happy with everything. They started to prep me for theatre. The hour had arrived.

Dr Mohan, a renowned kidney surgeon was the doctor that would carry out the transplant. My mam, two sisters and my girlfriend were in the hospital at this stage. I was due to go theatre at 3.00pm, but it was pushed to 4.00pm. I could see my family all getting as nervous as I was, but they were trying not to show it. My nerves kicked in around 3.30pm, 30 mins before lift off. I was weighing up everything in my mind. Would the operation go ok? Will my body take to the new organ? These thoughts started to race through my mind.

The nurse came in, attached my drip and gave me my pre-op injections. The hospital porters were patiently waiting to bring me down, keeping me calm. I was starting to get quite nervous, it was time...

The hospital porter started to slowly wheel me down when I just broke down in tears. They were tears of pure joy. I remember the last face I saw before I went into theatre, it was my mam's face and I was happy for her that her youngest son wouldn't have to go through dialysis anymore, and hopefully have a new life.

The operation took roughly four hours. It went very well by all accounts, and I remember waking up extremely groggy in my own room. They always put you in the recovery room before you go up to the public ward in a few days time. I spent the next three to four days there. The next few days were some of the hardest and most painful of my life but also the happiest. I knew in a few months, all going well, I would be a new man.

When you come out of theatre after a kidney transplant, it can be like starting again in a lot of departments. You have a lot of fluid on your chest and lungs, and you have to train your breathing with simple breathing exercises with an implement that looks like a baby's toy.

Due to the immense pain you are in, walking is an epic task. You have to take baby steps and not overdo it. You have been through a huge operation with a huge scar and you need to remember that if you don't go slowly it can set you back tenfold. I was given a morphine pump that you could press when the pain was bad. I think I nearly broke that pump. My levels were being closely monitored after the operation including my blood pressure and I nearly messed that up very quickly.

There are two common types of organ rejection:

Acute Rejection –
Usually occurs anytime during the first year after transplant and can usually be treated successfully.

Chronic Rejection –
Usually occurs slowly over a long period of time. The causes are not well understood and treatment is often not successful.

The funny but scary story is that the next day after the operation, my brother came up to see me and a friend after him. I had secretly asked them both to bring me up some Lucozade as I was parched with thirst and I drank the two bottles one after another in quick succession. Little did I realise that I was only supposed to be drinking water. The Lucozade had a wild reaction to my levels and I was as high as a kite from the sugar. My levels were all over the place.

The doctors and nurses had to literally make me go cold turkey for the next day or so and wean me off the sugar like a drug addict to get my levels back to normal. That was a scary few days and I was told off, which again I totally deserved. I never did that again.

I remember vividly it was New Year's Eve, going into 2008, two days after the operation. A new year with new possibilities and for me, a new life. I remember feeling quite lonely at 12.00am watching television, looking at all the celebrations going on all over the world, people happily ringing in the new year. I cried my eyes out. They were tears of joy, but I also felt sad and lonely, as I thought about my dad a lot when all this was happening. I knew that he was looking after me and still to this day he keeps an eye on the family to make sure we are all okay.

I had tubes sticking out from everywhere for the first few days and then one or two were disconnected as I got stronger. I was encouraged to get up and move if I was able, even if it meant just walking down the corridor and back. The one attachment I hated was the catheter. It was connected through my penis and it was the bane of my life. It's main function is to drain urine from the urinary bladder as in urinary catheterization, e.g., the intermittent catheters or Foley catheter or even when the urethra is damaged as in suprapubic catheterisation. I know it was a necessary evil, as it was acting for my bladder, but it made simple tasks like showering and dressing, etc., a huge effort, and I despised it.

I remember one time when I was so frustrated with it that when the male nurse who used to come in and check on me in the my private room, came in that morning, I actually offered him €500 to take it out there and then. The final straw came one night when I must have turned over suddenly in my sleep and I ripped the tip of my penis. I woke up the next morning and my pyjamas were covered in blood. This was the only morning I was a bad patient, as I demanded quite loudly I had had enough, and the blood and the pain being the clincher.

Day by day, I was getting a lot stronger and eating. I was taking small walks too but minding not to overdo it. I was starting to feel human again and as always, with the constant stream of visitors, I wanted to be stronger to be able to talk to them. They were coming to see how I was doing and they were there to wish me well. I was very tired, but I was very happy to see them.

The doctors and their team did their usual rounds and did their poking and prodding and they seemed happy with my progress, which I was delighted about.

They decided I would be moved to the public ward, as I well and strong enough to do so. I was secretly overjoyed about this. It was lonely in the recovery room on your own sometimes and anyone that knows me, knows I'm a chatterbox, so I like lots of interaction with people.

The next day I was moved and it was so much brighter in the room, a welcome change. I was sharing the ward with another eight or so people that were a lot older than me, but I didn't care, as it was company.

I spent my days reading and binging on DVDs when people were not visiting. I was trying to get stronger everyday. I slowly morphed into the newspaper boy, as I would get the papers from the downstairs shop for the older men that weren't as physically active on the ward, plus it was bit of exercise for me.

The nights were a tad tricky for sleeping, as you had a chorus of snores from all corners, but I eventually found out that the wonder of sleeping pills was an option.

I was a very happy transplant recipient after that, a good night's sleep was a luxury. My body was trying to get used to the immunosupressant drugs which at the start caused me to have crazy dreams and broken sleep. It would leave me exhausted during the day. I was also woken early every morning for breakfast and I would be checked on during the night for blood pressure checks.

I was delighted that the kidney was reacting well and very happy that the doctors were pleased with my recovery. There was like-minded people around me to chat to too if I was unsure about anything.

The staff and doctors in Beaumont Hospital are second to none. A lot of people slag off the healthcare system in Ireland, but I have only ever received top class care from all departments.

All the information that I had to digest back then and for the future was very overwhelming. It was a lot to take in about the scope of my medication all at once. The amount I would be taking for life and what they are all for, but as I have always said it was a small price to pay for the new healthy life I was hopefully about to embark on.

Your medication is your lifeline and anyone who is on medication should remember that. After a year with my kidney I made the mistake of not realising how important my medication is, but I will tell you about that later on.

It took me a few days, weeks and months to get my head around everything I had to remember for the future and if they had asked me to read *War and Peace* cover to cover, I would have. I didn't want to mess anything up.

After 13 days or so, I was allowed to go home, as I was a lot stronger. The way it works after that is you have to return to the hospital everyday for the next week or two after the operation for health checks and to get your dressing changed. My mam was like my chauffeur for those few weeks, God bless her.

When my stitches were finally out, I was given all the dressings and it was up to me to look after everything, but the hospital as always was amazing. If I ever had a question about anything, they were there to answer it. The visits to the hospital were still very regular, but just not everyday.

Now, I was under strict instructions not to go back to my job at Dell for at least three months. Even though it wasn't a hard labour job, you still had to rest and recuperate and let your scar heal.

I went back after six weeks, as I am not a great man for sitting still. I do want to say that the company was amazing to me during the whole process and I thank them dearly for it.

Chapter 10

A monumental mistake

All my life, I have always being proactive towards quirky business ideas and I always wanted to run my own business. I had, in the few months previous to the operation invested in a chocolate fountain machine for weddings and events, after I had seen one at an event I had been at the year before. I had a website designed and this was the birth of the infamous Seacláid Chocolate Fountains.

It was the first time I dipped my toe into the business pond, a side business for the time being anyway as I still had my job at Dell.

Obviously, the operation played a huge part in my life, but I was determined to make this business work. It was a great outlet for me while I was convalescing in my mam's house.

I wanted to build and build up Seacláid Chocolate Fountains to be a great success and I will always remember my business phone buzzing on my mam's coffee table with booking enquiries coming in, while I was sat there in pyjamas and a dressing gown trying to get better after the operation.

I was so proud of putting it all together myself, and now here I had a fully fledged small start up and my goal was to make it work.

Thankfully, I had set it up just in time. The downturn in the economy kicked off in 2008 and 22 of us were let go from our jobs at Dell in the middle of 2008. They had decided to move the design side of the business to Copenhagen. We weren't the first company that this had happened to and we surely wouldn't be the last.

The recession hit the world badly back then and companies suffered worldwide. As I type this in 2021, the economy is still reeling from it in certain professions, along with the Covid-19 global pandemic we are in. Even though I had this new business back then I still had to look for another job during the day. I was still building it up and most of the work was weekend-based with weddings and parties.

I eventually secured a position with what I thought was a reputable event business and I found out much to my own detriment that it was the catalyst for me nearly losing my transplanted kidney and going back to square one.

In brief, it was nine months of pure stress and rising blood pressure through false promises being made, chasing wages every week and it turned out to be a horrible period of my life. The place was run by a cowboy of epic proportions.

During these months I was stupidly forgetting to take my medication as regularly as I should have been. Little did I know how much of a monumental mistake that was.

I paid a high price for my absent mindedness nearly a year after the operation and ended up back in hospital for over a week where they had to administer a very high dose of steroids and various other methods to save my transplanted kidney.

When you get an organ transplanted into your body, the white blood cells in your body fight against it as they regard the organ as a foreign body that shouldn't be there. That is where the anti-rejection drugs come in. They fight against the white blood cells rejecting the organ.

I hadn't been taking mine as regularly and regimentally as I should have and the kidney was very close to being rejected. My doctor Dr Conlon told me that in only another few days I would have been back to square one. Thankfully they caught it in time. I didn't make that mistake again, and I never will.

To anyone that might be reading this that is on the way to getting a transplant or taking any kind of anti-rejection drugs, I cannot stress enough how important they are for your well-being, and the longevity of your kidney and your life.

It was nearing the end of 2008 and my first year with the new kidney. It was an eventful one. Apart from the huge glitch of nearly losing the kidney, I was feeling positive about the future.

The downside was my relationship had ended with my girlfriend, probably due the stress I was under that year with the dreadful job and getting let go from Dell.

She will remain anonymous but I would never have gotten through the transplant operation without her and the following months after it, so if you are reading this, thank you from the bottom of my heart.

Business was ticking over with Seacláid Chocolate Fountains. I had also secured a new job in Reads Design & Print in Sandyford as a senior graphic designer in their new design studio and I was loving it. They were a great company to work for and I was kept very busy with that. I was really settling back into life. The first year is always hard after a big operation especially given the magnitude of a kidney transplant. They were very accommodating with days off for checkups. I was looking to the future with optimism and still couldn't believe I was so lucky twice with the kidney.

I went on to work as a freelance social media manager for Reads Design & Print, as I still stay in touch with my former boss and friend Niall Mescall, who is managing director there.

My daughter, Amelia, and my mam, ladies who lunch

Amelia and I on a little daddy-daughter day out

My mam on one of our mammy/son nights out.

Jen, wifey, my rock, at her happiest, gin in hand

On one of our many family trips to the beach

Mama's boys, myself & Niall

Our beautiful dogs, Ellie and Lulu Kirwan

On Amelia's 8th birthday, her 2nd birthday in lockdown, during the COVID-19 global pandemic.

My two beautiful daughters, Nicole, 23, and Amelia Lily, 8.

Chapter 11
Anything is possible

It was now mid-2009, the singing was never too far away, and back at the start of 2008 while I recuperating in my mam's house, after the operation, I had written a song to pass the time. I had written it about my whole kidney journey much like I am doing now but in song form. It tells the story of my journey from diagnosis to dialysis to post transplant, and how much your life can change for the better.

I named the song 'Anything is possible', and that is a mantra I still stand by to this day, that if you put your mind to anything and believe in yourself, you can do ANYTHING.

I had the melody in my head as I was writing it. I don't play an instrument, so I needed a producer to make this dream come alive. I had worked with a guy before on something else. I approached him and told him my vision. Lee Boylan is his name. He runs Inglewood Studios in Clonsilla and is one of the most talented people I have ever come across.

He took onboard what I was saying and we had a chat and set down some ideas. Lee got to work and when he came back to me with the first draft of music to accompany the lyrics I was delighted to say the least. We tweaked it over the next few weeks and then low and behold we had the final product. We recorded an instrumental version and an acoustic version of it. It was exactly what I wanted. 'Anything is possible', the song, the anthem was alive and kicking.

I then had another idea, a pipe dream if you will. The World Transplant Games were being held in Dublin the following year in 2010. We were nearing the end of 2009. I got in touch with the Irish Kidney Association. We had a great chat and the idea was born for me to perform my song at the opening ceremony in The Helix theatre in Dublin the following August.

This was amazing news. I couldn't believe it, I would be performing in front of a few hundred people, people like me, that were post-transplant, that were competing in these fantastic games, people from all over the world. This was a dream come true, but I knew I needed something to add some spectacle to this amazing chance I was given to perform on such a big stage in the O'Mahony Hall in The Helix.

I contacted an incredibly talented group of people called 'the Dublin Gospel Choir' about hopefully, maybe backing me when I perform. I was completely chancing my arm but again, God smiled down and they accepted. These guys are renowned for their talent worldwide and have had many top selling albums. They played all the big festivals in Ireland including Electric Picnic.

As well as being super talented, these guys are the nicest group of people you will ever meet.

I handed the backing track over to them and left it with them. A few weeks later I got a call to ask could I come up and hear what they had done with it.

Wow... I was delighted with what they came up with, that lovely gospel sound that I had envisaged in my head. I still couldn't believe that my song was now alive and I was going to perform at such a prestigious ceremony. I had numerous rehearsals with them and we were ready to go.

Finally, the event date came around and I was so nervous, but we had rehearsed it over and over so I was happy enough. I was up in the dressing rooms before the performance and I couldn't believe how relaxed the Dublin Gospel Choir were. I took something from that day for my future singing career to come.

On stage in The Helix with the amazing Dublin Gospel Choir

Again, I had that feeling of dread, thinking about walking out on to a big stage to a large crowd but what a fantastic venue the O' Mahony Hall in The Helix was. I had been there before but only in the audience.

This time I was the performer and the audience were people on the same journey that I had been on and still on to this day. I hoped the lyrics and the song jumped out to somebody in the crowd. Mary Kennedy, the RTÉ television presenter, was the MC that day.

We had to wait in the wings until we were called out and this wasn't helping my nerves any. It was finally time to go out and Mary introduced us onto the stage. The intro started to play and we walked out one by one and the nerves just lifted. I think it was because of who I was performing to, as I felt that they might appreciate what they heard and the sentiment of the song.

The sound of the Dublin Gospel Choir was breathtaking behind me. This was second nature to them, but I was a newbie of sorts at performing on this scale. It was an original song, not one the audience recognised easily, so that gave me a chance to march to my own beat.

The last line 'Anything is Possible' rang out in the large theatre. This was met with rapturous applause and cameras flashing, which I have to say I enjoyed immensely. A big dream of mine had come true and it was only the beginning. I was on a high that day that took me a while to come down from.

That same song ended up being played all across Australia years later, after a chance meeting with an Irish DJ called Declan O'Callaghan. He was living in Australia and happened to be home for a wedding and he had heard me in a venue I was playing in. He asked me for a CD which thankfully I had with me on the night. Over the next few weeks, I did two live radio interviews with Declan O'Callaghan live on Australia radio and both interviews were played all across Australia.

An online magazine in Australia also requested 20 copies of an album I had recorded, *In Full Swing* (a collection of my favourite swing classics). These albums were given out as prizes in an online competition. This was all happening so fast and I was loving it to be quite honest.

I did one of the radio interviews while staying in the Malton Hotel in Killarney. I had been booked for a very prestigious gig and here I was in a beautiful suite, talking to a radio presenter in Australia. This was where the next chapter of my life had brought me.

This had firmly instilled the love of music back into me, which in turn would lead to a brand new chapter and fantastic things to come in my life. I was on an exciting journey that would bring me places I never even dreamed of.

I am still very proud to this day of that song and I hope to perform it on the big stage again someday very soon.

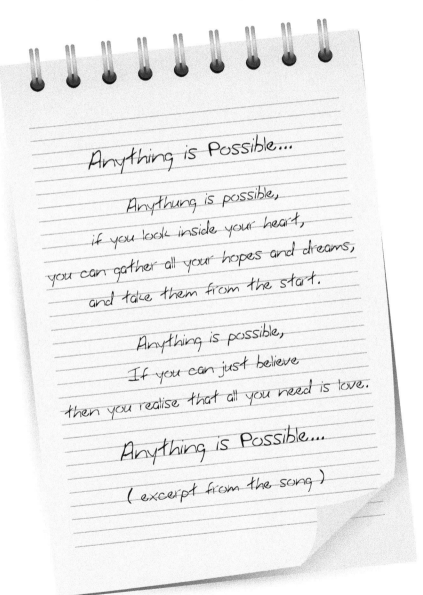

Anything is Possible....

Anythung is possible,
if you look inside your heart,
you can gather all your hopes and dreams,
and take them from the start.

Anything is possible,
If you can just believe
then you realise that all you need is love.

Anything is Possible....

(excerpt from the song)

Chapter 12
The birth of my alter ego

This new life that I was enjoying gave me so much belief in myself and I felt if I put my mind to it, I could achieve anything. They say that a few times in your life you can have a light bulb moment where you come up with a great idea that develops into something bigger and bigger, and continues to grow to become a huge part of your life.

My lightbulb moment, well one of them, came as I was out with my family one night.

Each year, for my dad's anniversary we go out for a meal. This night in particular we went to an Asian restaurant called ZAO Fusion in Santry, Dublin. We had been there many times before and they usually had karoake on, so inevitably I would get up and sing a few tunes.

This night was a little different. When I entered with my family, the owner asked me would I sing a few more than usual, as the karoake MC had gastroenteritis. I was happy to oblige.

The night with the family was great as usual, as nights out with my family always are and I was getting up at intervals to sing. By the last four songs, people had finished eating and had turned their chairs around, listening to me intently. I was buzzing.

90

I had for years wanted to get back into singing in a big way, but I didn't know what angle to adopt, as you have to have a product to sell to procure gigs for yourself, either independently or through a promoter.

My love for swing music had grown dramatically, and I was listening to Michael Bublé, the canadian crooner a lot. I had seen him in 2005 in the Point Depot as it was called back then and I was hooked. I couldn't get enough of this guys songs and the arrangements of all the old classics. The last song I sang that night in ZAO Fusion was Michael Bublé's 'Home'.

I got home that night and was racking my brain and I came up with the idea for a Michael Bublé tribute act. There was only one or two doing something similar but nothing major. After hours of lost sleep that night trying to think of a name for the act, I eventually fell asleep.

The next morning I woke up and the name for the act came to me, 'FRANKLY BUBLÉ'. It would encompass Frank Sinatra and Michael Bublé and everything in between. I had all these ideas running around in my head and it was a little bit overwhelming but also very exciting.

It was 2010, and I went gung-ho with this idea. I started getting all my marketing done for it. Thankfully, being a graphic designer and working for a printers, I had all this at my disposal.

The next step was to get a sound engineer, buy great quality backing tracks and structure this idea before I unveiled it to the public. I also wanted to create a professional website to accompany my endeavour.

With my lifelong pal since kindergarten, Noel Murphy

The website was beautifully designed by my kindergarten friend Noel Murphy. The website was aptly named www.franklybuble.com.

I have known him all my life and he is one of life's gentlemen. He is still a very good friend of mine to this day and we speak regularly.

Next, I got in touch with a good friend of mine called Conor Burke, to assist with sound engineering duties. It just so happens that Conor is a transplant recipient too. I told him my vision and how I wanted it to be. I asked him if it was workable. He is the ultimate professional and assured me it wasn't a problem.

Conor became one of my greatest allies, both musically and personally, and I still count him as a very good friend today. He's a fantastic guy and a great father.

My health was thriving and my health check-ups were tri-monthly and still are to this day. I am delighted to say that my levels have been constantly spot on for the last 14 years except 2008, when I nearly lost the kidney through my own carelessness with my medication. Besides what happened in 2008, I am able to maintain my levels by looking after myself, looking after my diet, and adopting an 'everything in moderation' approach. And most of all, being regimental with my medication.

Early Frankly Bublé promo shot

This whole 'FRANKLY BUBLÉ' thing blew up like I never imagined. When I felt ready I put on my first show which in The Ashbourne House in Co. Meath, very near to Ratoath, where I live to this day.

My first show was a sell out. It probably wasn't my most stellar performance but it still sold out. I couldn't believe it.

Only a few months after my first gig, I was already planning another show, this time in the Carlton Airport Hotel in Dublin, (now known the Clayton Hotel). At this stage, I had brought my pal Luke Thomas into the fold as an extra singer on the shows. He ended up being a permanent fixture on the shows for the next few years.

While I was planning the show, I got a phone call from a company called Planit Management enquiring about my availability for the unofficial after-parties for the 2010 Michael Bublé concerts in the Aviva stadium. These gigs were being held in the bar in The Burlington as it was known back then (now known the Clayton Hotel, Burlington Road). I nearly fell off the chair... me singing at the unofficial after parties for my idol. How did this even happen?

The plan was that we would be playing to concert goers, post concert for the two nights that Michael Bublé was playing. I was in a state of disbelief. I was pinching myself constantly.

Both gigs turned out to be absolutely amazing, as the people were great and really got into it. It filled us with encouragement and enthusiasm. The two nights couldn't have gone better and that is really where the 'FRANKLY BUBLÉ' brand started to grow.

At an early photoshoot with my pal, Luke Thomas, always acting the goat.

Above and below: Onstage at The Button Factory, 2015

Above and left: On the set of a Facebook Live event in 2021; Luke and I have always had this instant, natural chemistry on stage.

With super-star Gavin James, after his gig in Whelan's pub, in 2018

With Gavin James after his gig in Croke Park supporting Ed Sheeran

With former model turned mindfulness coach, Alison Canavan

With TV personality, Grainne Seoige

With my pal celebrity/wedding photographer, Jenny McCarthy

The phone started to call then with people looking to book us. Again, I couldn't believe this was happening to me. After all, I had considered myself to be on a run of bad luck, what with being so sick in the last few years. This was a welcome injection of positivity into my life. My dreams were manifesting right in front of me. It really felt like I was finally experiencing of streak of good luck.

I knew then I had something very marketable, and I knew I had to build on it. Subsequent sell out shows followed in various venues and hotels. I was just pinching myself every time.

I constantly wanted to strive for better and be the busiest tribute artist on the scene. A few promoters had been ringing. I was adamant that I wanted to stay independent. I tried out a few but it was always the same end product on their parts, greed and stupidity, so I settled on two good promoters in the end and we still have a great relationship to this day. These promoters were very honest and you knew where you stood with them at all times, and we developed a good working relationship. The phone continued to hop-off the line and before I knew it, I was gigging three weekends out of four a month.

It was early 2011, around February, and the next pinch me moment happened. Michael Bublé had decided to launch his infamous *Christmas* album in the flagship fashion store Brown Thomas that year. Between Brown

Thomas and Michael's record company, they decided to have four different artists performing Christmas songs from Michael's new album in store in October to celebrate the launch. All the crooner classics.

I got a phone call from my friend Noel Murphy, who works for Michael's record company asking would I be interested.

'Am I interested?' I exclaimed down the phone in disbelief.

I'm note sure how many times I swore during that phone call but the answer to his question was a resounding YES! This gig would stand me in good stead early the following year.

At this point, I was laughing at the amount of good luck coming my way, and then I stopped and took stock of all the hard work I had put into creating the brand. I gave myself a small pat on the back too, anytime anything positive happened. The secret in this game is to be humble, stay humble. Another mantra that I live by today.

The weekend in Brown Thomas was a fantastic one and again, heightened my profile as a singer and artist. The amount of business that it brought was astounding. The brand was growing stronger, day by day.

At the same time that everything was on a roll with the gigging, Jennie and I were going great. I had met Jennie on a night in 2009, whilst out with friends. I wasn't particularly looking for anything at the time, but we clicked and she was a lovely girl, very easy to talk to and I needed that.

We arranged to meet up for a cinema date and it started from there. Little did I know I would marry this girl over two years later. The rest, as they say, is history.

I had eventually moved back to my own house after having rented it out for two years while I was on dialysis, and by this stage, Jennie and I had moved in together. We had spoken briefly about the next stage in our lives, the M word... marriage, but nothing had been set in stone yet.

We hadn't been together for years like most couples but it just felt right. We were like polar opposites. Jennie is from Greystones and is a warm, caring person with a quieter nature than me, in stark contrast to my brash, joker -self hailing proudly from Santry on Dublin's Northside. Opposites attract as they say, but it just worked and still does to this day.

In the background and on the sly I had been looking at wedding ring designs for inspiration but I wasn't going to act on anything for a while.

I was enjoying living together, as I had always lived on my own in my house, but when Jennie moved in she instantly made my house a home. She instantly made me want to be the best partner I could be for her and after all the madness that had gone on in my life over the last few years, she was a wonderful influence on my life, and she continues to be to this day.

I was also far too busy to start planning anything in the marriage/engagement department at that stage, so it was put on the back burner for the next few months. Ironically, I had being booked for the Fitzpatrick's Castle Christmas shows that year, the same hotel in Killiney that I was playing in on the night I received my kidney in 2007.

I was still looking at wedding ring designs and I then started to put a small plan in place for the following year. A wedding proposal.

Chapter 13

The big question

It was all go this year, in March, 2011. I did what I had planned to do for a while. Propose to Jennie.

I booked a weekend away for Jennie and I to the Hotel Kilkenny. I had been so busy and we were due a few days away. What Jennie didn't know was I had been onto the hotel manager and had arranged for a song to be played during our meal the night I was going to get down on bended knee. The song was a beautiful one called 'You and I', a Stevie Wonder song recorded by Michael Bublé.

It was nearly a false start when they played the song at the wrong time. Panicked, I had to try covertly alert the staff of the mishap, and I tried nodding my head to get them to play the song. Looking back it was quite comical...

They, embarrassed themselves, then played it at the right time. Initially, the music was very faint but they soon realised that it was too low and increased the volume so that it could be heard throughout the restaurant. The time had come for me to pop the question.

So on I went and got down on my knee and I asked the burning question, 'Will you marry me?'

She said Yes! Thank god, after all the organisation and in front of a packed restaurant, she did, otherwise, it may have been quite embarrassing and very awkward.

The next few months as you can imagine went into overdrive with wedding planning. We decided we weren't going to wait till the following year and decided on a very poignant date.

The date we picked was 29th December, 2011, four years to the day that I received my kidney transplant. We both thought it would be very special, and at least I will never forget our wedding anniversary.

We never had any desire to kill each other through the whole preparation, which is quite rare. We decided on what tasks we would look after and that. The wedding preparation went ahead without any hassle.

We picked our bridesmaids and groomsmen. I was delighted that Nicole, who was now 13, was going to be a bridesmaid. This was a very special thing for me on our big day.

We picked the Park Hotel in Newtown Mount Kennedy, as Jennie was a Greystones native. It had a beautiful big room and it would nicely house our 130 guests. We picked my pal Luke's band, The Swing Cats, as our wedding band for the night.

I picked the song 'Everything' by Michael Bublé to sing to my new wife during the evening wedding reception as the lyrics are quite special to us. We had first dance to 'You and I' by Michael Bublé, the song I proposed to Jennie with.

Before we knew it, it was November and I was busy rehearsing for a jam-packed schedule in December. All the wedding planning had been done and we had very little to check-off the to-do list.

I still couldn't believe that I was actually getting married. I was never the settling down type and honestly I didn't think I would meet someone that I could see myself settling with, neither did my dad, Lord rest him.

Jennie and I taken some well needed time out on our wedding day

Our wedding day had finally come around... I stayed the night before in my mam's house and went for the obligatory 'last night as a single man' pints. I was very relaxed about it all.

I slept like a baby that night, but when I woke up the nerves kicked in tenfold. I can't explain why. I guess I hadn't seen the day ever happening. I was overwhelmed by it all.

The newly-weds

I nibbled at my breakfast, which I never do. After my breakfast, I put my runners and training gear on and I went out for an intended short walk. I ended up doing about eight kilometres, but it completely cleared my head and put me in a nice relaxed state for the special day ahead. I felt so lucky to be in the position of getting this chance to marry the woman I loved. With all the negative stuff that had gone on in my life I assumed it was never going to be on the cards for me.

All of a sudden it was like someone hit the fast forward button. Things started to go at a mile a minute. My wedding party started texting me asking what the arrangements and times were. My brother Niall arrived at my mam's house with a great little present for me. Jack Daniel's would be my bourbon of choice if I have one. It was an engraved Jack Daniel's hip flask which was exactly what I needed on the morning and believe me, I took full advantage of it.

The minutes were ticking on and it was nearly time to get going. Nobody knows this next fact but when I went up to have my shower I spent the best part of it crying my eyes out over my dad. He would have loved the day and he would have been in deep shock that I was actually getting married. I really felt his absence on my wedding day. He was such a big character that everyone that knows him missed him that day, none more so than my family and I.

The weather that day was dire, very windy and rainy. After all it was the end of December so we knew that it wouldn't be great but I guess we hoped the sun might have come out for our big day but it wasn't to be. I rang my daughter Nicole to make sure she was okay as she slept in Jennie's mam's house that night. and she was loving it. The hairdressers and make-up artists were starting to arrive to do all the bridal party and Nicole was loving it all.

A few of my mam's neighbours had come in to wish me well and it was great craic in the house, which took my mind off everything. They knew me as a kid and as an adult, being a messer all the time, so I think they were actually glad that someone was finally making an honest man out of me.

It was time to go. My mam, my brother and I went in the one car. We were getting married in a church in Greystones where Jennie had lived all her life.

All was going great until that moment when it was time for Jennie to walk up the aisle, and the beautiful voice of Sarah Waldron, our church singer and personal friend, rang through the church with the stunning 'Flower Duet'. Seemingly, according to sources, any bit of colour I had in my face completely drained and I was as white as a sheet, plus, Jennie was in the porch nearly getting sick with nerves. She wouldn't be one for attention in any shape or form. The thought of walking up the aisle was killing her. We were some pair on the day.

But we got down to business and everything went according to plan. There were tears of joy and laughter on the altar. It was a very relaxed ceremony in the end and everyone had a great day and evening, where we bopped until the early hours to the sound of The Swing Cats and my DJ pal, Geoff Duffy, brought all the guests into the early hours.

My new wife Jennie and some of my nearest and dearest friends

I am embarrassed to say that I was in bed and all for 12.30p.m. The day got the better of me and I had to bow out but the party kept going until 6.30am.

The next day when we surfaced and went down to meet all the guests at breakfast, I felt fine and we said a big thanks to everyone, and we set off for home. As we were pulling off, I felt so unwell that we had to stop the car three times on the way home, as I thought I was going to get sick. This progressively got worse as the journey went on and when I got home I was like death warmed up. I seemed to pass whatever bug I had over the course of the day onto Jennie and we basically spent the next two days oscillating between the bed and the bathroom. What a way to start married life!

But we are still together today, strong as ever, and now we have an addition in our house, Amelia Lily Kirwan. She arrived on St Patrick's Day, 2013. Amelia, or Millie as she is better known, is a pure character and has brought so much fun, love and happiness to our house, so much so, that we couldn't imagine how we were without her. We must tell each other we love each other about 50 times a day and she is as bright and intelligent as she is funny and crazy.

I never believed I would be blessed with two beautiful, healthy children and a loving, caring wife such as Jennie, but God has been good to me. In fairness, he had a bit of making up to do.

My daughter, Nicole, and I on my wedding day. Nicole was a bridesmaid on the day, which was special to me.

With my beautiful mam on my wedding day

A soulmate is a person with whom one has a feeling of deep or natural affinity.

This may involve similarity, love, romance, platonic relationships, comfort, intimacy, compatibility and trust.

These are the all the qualities that my wife, Jennie possesses, and I feel very lucky to have found her. I look forward to many more happy years together.

110

Chapter 14

The next chapter –
Time to educate the mind

In 2014, I decided to challenge myself again and go back to college at night. I always loved learning new skills and facts, and I really challenged myself by doing a diploma course in website design, a diploma in digital marketing and a certificate in social media, simultaneously. Throw a new baby into the equation, plus a day job and singing at the weekends and well you can gather it was quite busy. I relished it.

There was a lot of study and research involved, but with good time management, I or should I say, we managed. Without a good support network you can't really chase certain dreams or aspirations. As I said earlier, since the operation the word CANNOT rarely comes into my vocabulary, especially when it concerns achieving the goals I set for myself. I even try nowadays to do a course a year. I never want to stop learning as long as I live, plus it keeps your mind alive.

I started the website design course first in Dublin Business School. It was all new to me as it was a lot of coding, which I had never had much experience with but I stuck with it. I hate to fail at anything.

I was so nervous about the exam that I messed up early on during it and I only noticed half way through when I went to test the project. I had to start again, but between the jigs and the reels, I got the project to work again. I think that impressed the tutor, although I shouldn't have messed up in the first place. Strangely enough, I never did anything much with the skill after the course. As for the digital marketing course, that was a completely different story I loved it.

With my mam on Graduation night

I was proud as punch to graduate with a first class honours

I did the digital marketing course in the European Institute of Communications and the content was amazing. I was hooked right through the course. I was the one asking all the questions in the class. I wanted to know everything there was to know, as I knew if I did this right I could make a business from it.

The tutor in question was a lady called Ciamh McCrory. We are still fantastic friends today. She made the course very interesting and fun, and that's why I managed to get the mark I did.

All the graduates on the night – a fantastic night that I won't forget in a hurry

Ciamh is hugely popular in the digital world today and has featured as a speaker at many different digital summits. She has made appearences on a chat show called Midday, as well as being the digital lead for Insight Consultants. She lives in Dubai now and continues to become increasingly successful.

I put my heart and soul into the project at the end and I received a first class honours in my diploma, which I was over the moon about. It just showed that the hard work, research and long hours had paid off.

My former lecturer, friend, and general all round legend, Ciamh McCrory

I went onto to create a small freelance business using my social media and digital skills as a part of it. A big thanks to Ciamh McCrory, Eugene Grey and the European Institute of Communications.

Since then I have always kept my nose in the digital world due to my digital and social clients. I have since gone on to study more online courses with the Shaw Academy in order to further my skillset.

The reason I wanted to talk about my further education is that I want to encourage people that where or are in the same position as me to never think you cannot do it. Always follow your dreams and keep on learning.

Receiving my diploma from Eugene Grey, my friend, and
CEO of the European Institute of Communications

It doesn't matter what age you are or if you feel you
cannot do it, turn that into an 'I CAN' and believe me,
you won't regret it.

Chapter 15

Lucky man

I always felt so lucky for all these opportunities that were coming my way and I was always grateful whenever I got booked for a gig. Singing took me to amazing places and enabled me to be involved in many great events, numerous charity fundraisers, and much more.

Some of the fantastic highlights my love for singing and my alter ego 'FRANKLY BUBLÉ' had enabled me to do were:

1. A charity single for the homeless, the brain child of Shane Lynch of Boyzone fame.

2. Numerous charity fundraisers for cancer, autism, down syndrome, mental awareness, and many more.

3. I was flown over to Italy to sing at a wedding in a castle in the hills of Florence... magical!

4. I was asked to play in some of the country's most prestigious hotels and venues.

5. I was flown to New York and Las Vegas to sing in venues in both of these amazing locations.

6. I got the chance to play in some high profile concert venues Vicar Street, The Sugar Club and The Helix.

7. Duetting with Hollywood star, Michael Fassbender, and the video clip going viral.

8. Meeting my idol Michael Bublé in person in Las Vegas, which was a dream come true.

9. Getting my self-penned song 'Anything is possible' played all across Australia and doing interviews for various Australian radio stations.

These are only a few of the amazing things that have happened to me since my transplant. The one thing I had and still do to this day is self-belief. You should give anything you are passionate about a try, even if you fail at it, because failure is only one step closer to success.

I guess what I am trying to say here is, that people should never let a sickness or a big operation define them, that you should always have self-belief and confidence in yourself.

It has helped me in so many ways with my mental health, through both pre-transplant and post-transplant, more so post-transplant.

I feel extremely lucky and humbled to have been able to do these things, so if you have something you have always wanted to do... just do it!

You don't want to regret not doing or even trying something that you always wanted to. I definitely won't as I'm making sure all my dreams come true.

There are many wonderful things that have happened to me, that will stay with me for all my days. I would like to tell you about some of them, so get yourself a cup of tea or even a glass of wine, sit back, and indulge me for a little bit.

A charity single for the homeless community

What a weekend that was in the company of some of Ireland's top musicians, actors and celebrities

In 2013, I was asked to be part of a charity single for the homeless community spearheaded by Shane Lynch of Boyzone fame. Along with myself, there was a host of musicians, pop stars, celebrities, and TV stars.

The song was called 'One More for the Road'. It was an Irish tune with a rousing chorus in it, which was very catchy.

It was done over a weekend in April of that year, I think, and it was an amazing two days. There were friendships formed that day that are still strong.

Myself and Shane Lynch on the day

The process was amazing seeing everybody record their part and hearing it played back with Shane and the sound engineers watching over everything to make sure it all went smoothly. All the egos were left at the door those two days.

áire Ní Chuinneagáin, Edele Lynch and Sinead O' rroll of Irish band, B*Witched, and my good friend d singer Angel

The funny thing was a lot of people had only met for the first time but you would never know, as the camaraderie that we all encountered over those two days was unbelievable. It was like a mini-Live Aid, without the bank balances and Bob Geldof of course.

I felt privileged and honoured to be part of it. Unfortunately, the homeless situation is still at a very low ebb in Ireland and the numbers on the streets are still rising by the day.

An amazing wedding in a stunning castle in Florence

I will never forget the call coming in for this gig. A lovely guy called Wayne Finn rang me out of the blue and explained that he had seen Luke Thomas of The Swing Cats and I playing in a South Dublin pub called The Goat. Seemingly, the night when he saw us, he and his future wife agreed that when they got married they would have us to entertain all their guests. Well low and behold, they bloody well did.

I actually hung up the phone on Wayne thinking it was one of the lads taking the piss. He rang back and was completely genuine about the proposition to perform at his wedding. I was gob-smacked! It was another 'pinch me' moment, I couldn't believe what I was being asked.

I said to Wayne, 'So, let me get this straight, you are going to fly Luke and I over to beautiful Florence, put us up, pay for our transport, feed us, pay for our drink, rent out a top class music PA, and then pay us on top of that?'

You can see why I was sceptical and hung up.

Well, what an amazing time we had. I still think about it today!

We were flown over and arrived only to be put up in a beautiful hotel, like something out of a Hollywood film. It was about a 30 second walk away from a beautiful square in Florence with carousels and all different kinds of artists at each corner of the square. We arrived and got our barings, showered, and sauntered on up to the beautiful square that evening. Such an elegant, classy, romantic place. We had a great evening with the couple and their fantastic families, enjoying delicious food and drink, and listening to beautiful music.

We had the next day off, and we walked around and saw what beautiful Florence had to offer. It didn't disappoint. We sampled the fabulous cuisine and vino of course. It's a place that I fell in love with straight away, and a place I will return to again someday.

The next day, it was business time. I was up early and went for my morning walk. Again, I saw parts of Florence I hadn't seen the previous day and was wowed again. This was postcard stuff, so picturesque.

About 1.00pm, when Luke eventually got out of bed, we were collected by a taxi, and driven up to a castle in the hills of Florence. Yes, a castle! Even though I have travelled, this is stuff I had only seen in a fantasy, romance or gangster film. I kept pinching myself to make sure this wasn't a dream, even if it was a dream I was enjoying it.

So there we are, in 28 degrees heat or more, standing in the castle grounds, while the sound engineers set up our top of the range PA equipment so that we could

Luke Thomas and I posing for a photo in a castle in the hills of Florence.

do a soundcheck before that evening, when the wedding was taking place. We kept laughing at this, saying, 'how the hell did this happen?'

We had a great soundcheck and we were ready for that evening. We couldn't wait. So back to the hotel we went, got ourselves sorted – suited and booted, and back to the castle we went. As any band will tell you, always anticipate a wait at weddings to go on, so we were having a few drinks on the terrace and the father of the bride came down and insisted that we go up and dine with the family during the wedding dinner. This was such a beautiful gesture.

We were nearly falling asleep after the big meal and we still had to perform, but the show must go on and we had a great night. The hills of Florence were swinging. and Luke then brought the wedding party into the early hours with a DJ set, while I sipped cocktails with the crowd. What an experience, what lovely people and a definite 'pinch me moment'. There are a few more of them to come.

Meeting Michael Bublé in Las Vegas

As I was telling you earlier, in October, 2011, global superstar and Canadian crooner, Michael Bublé, was launching his now infamous 'Christmas' album in the Brown Thomas in Dublin and I was asked to be one of four acts to sing the weekend of the launch in the beautiful grand hall in Brown Thomas. I was set to perform songs from Michael Bublé, Frank Sinatra, Dean Martin, and many more. What a weekend, and what an honour and privilege it was to be asked. Jennie and I had gotten married in December, 2017, but our honeymoon wasn't until January 28th and we had booked a great honeymoon travelling to Las Vegas, New York and San Francisco.

First stop was Las Vegas. We were staying in the famous MGM Grand, which has been the mainstage for many a concert, boxing match and film over the decades. The place was out of this world. In Vegas, everything is so loud and big, and I loved every minute of it.

One particular evening we had planned to go for dinner in TAO restaurant in the Venetian Hotel, another hotel that has been featured in many a film.

Jennie has a habit of being fashionably late, and she wasn't going to break that trend while she was getting ready.

So I'm sitting downstairs in the MGM Grand waiting and watching the world go by, when low and behold, this figure presents himself in front of me lighting a cigarette. I did a double take, triple take to make sure. It was the one and only Michael Bublé!

I was completely overwhelmed and shocked. My phone wasn't working in Las Vegas so I ran across the lobby in the MGM to use the house phone, which if you haven't been there, my goodness, it's very large. I rang our room and spoke to Jennie and asked here to bring her phone but to please hurry, although I probably didn't phrase it as calmly as that. Well God bless her, she ran down with her camera.

I was truly convinced that we had lost him and that I wouldn't get to meet him or get a picture with him. So we went on a mission to find Michael Bublé in the casino in the MGM Grand. I was so disappointed that I couldn't see him, when all of a sudden there he was, directly in front of me.

My next challenge was to get him to stop so as to chat to him or even get a picture, and I'm thinking what am I going to say to him?

'Hi Michael, can I ask you a question?' were the immortal words I uttered. How original!

Michael Bublé and I in the MGM Grand, Las Vegas

I was met with a cautious face from Michael Bublé, which is understandable with the crazy goings-on in the world today.

I tried to mention a bit of familiar ground to try make him stay there long enough to get a picture but none of it worked.

I just mentioned about the Christmas album being launched in October in 2011 in Dublin and he seemed to relax as he knew what I was talking about. He was happy enough to stay for a picture. We had a quick chat and he thanked me for being involved in the launch of the album in Ireland, which was lovely to hear.

Two quite loud fans spotted him then and I politely thanked him, shook his hand, and I skipped off, happy as a clam. I just met my idol and he was a complete gent.

Duetting with Hollywood star Michael Fassbender

Most people will know the name Michael Fassbender from a Guinness advert from years ago, right up to the *X-Men* franchise and many other Hollywood blockbusters.

I must admit I knew of him and would have watched a few films, but he was never on my radar. It was nothing to do with his acting ability, I guess I just didn't know enough about him or his films.

In early 2016, I got a call from a pal of mine, Emer Corridan, who worked in the beautiful Malton Hotel in Killarney. Emer had booked me before over the years. She was now working in the Cahernane Hotel in Killarney. She called and asked was I free for a gig the following October and I said yes, but I also enquired about the gig.

She informed me that Michael Fassbender would be there and he would be receiving a special and very well respected accolade called the Order Of Inishfallen in the beautiful Europa Hotel. It has has been bestowed on many a worthy recipient down through the years.

The Order of Innisfallen is a renowned award which recognises contributions made to the economy of Killarney by various people from different industries and professions.

Michael Fassbender was being honoured by the town's Chamber of Tourism and Commerce, and the Killarney Municipal Area for helping to boost Killarney's profile on a world stage by achieving great success in his career.

The 44-year-old Kerryman has been nominated for the Academy Awards, Golden Globes and Baftas.

Previous recipients of the Order of Innisfallen include singer Daniel O'Donnell who has attracted thousands to his concerts in Killarney every year, businesswoman Isolde Liebherr, Margaret Cahill, the former head of Tourism Ireland Europe, and Brian Stack of CIE Tours.

Michael would have lived some of his younger life in Killarney, and he has put it firmly on the map through his work.

It was a very prestigious ceremony, with over 400 people in attendance and I was absolutely over the moon to be a part of it. I was honoured and privileged to be asked.

I had a few mishaps on the way down, getting lost, my sat nav sending me the wrong way and running out of petrol, but I got there by the skin of my teeth and got set up. Phew!

Little did I know what would unfold later on. It's something that would change my life in a sense and heighten my profile, but it all happened completely by accident. By God am I glad it did.

Whenever I was booked for a gig I always ask for the spec as in, whether it is up-tempo or background music, so when I enquired with Emer, she said it was to be nice background style music, so I took that onboard.

After a lot of waiting around with speeches from the chamber members and Michael himself, it was time to go on ... at 1.30am.

I was decked out in my black tuxedo for the event, and I started my set with mid-tempo swing and nice lounge-style background music staying true to the spec advised.

Michael Fassbender's parents and his wife, Swedish actress, Alicia Vikander, were also in attendance on the night. A member of their table kept trying to speak to me while I was singing, which can be quite annoying but seeing as who it was I entertained him, and he asked me would I play the Dean Martin classic 'That's Amore' for Michael Fassbender's dad.

I totally obliged and kicked into the swing classic. The crowd immediately reacted to it and got up to dance, as did Michael's parents, when it was coming to the end of the song, I asked Mr. Fassbender Snr if I should crank it up. His reply in his strong German accent was 'CRANK IT UP'.

I burst into 'Signed, Sealed, Delivered' by Stevie Wonder, and Michael and Alicia bounced up off their seats. Michael started making the 'we're not worthy' hand gestures towards me, made famous in *Wayne's World,* and I returned the gesture, making it a display of great craic had by all.

At this point, about 80% of the crowd were up on the dancefloor in front of the stage. I was loving this, as once I had quite a large crowd up dancing, plus a Hollywood A-Lister, I was doing something right. So my set continued with up-tempo numbers and I was really in the thick of it. The crowd were amazing and everybody was having a great time.

My next song was the classic floor filler, 'Proud Mary', and it was at this point in the night that Michael hopped up on stage to sing along.

Michael Fassbender and I on stage at the Europe Hotel, Killarney.

My next song was to be 'Suspicious Minds' by Elvis Presley, and I whispered to Michael to please stay on stage, which he did, thankfully and we did our infamous duet of the Elvis classic. Before the song started, I gestured to one of the chamber members and a friend of mine, Conor

Hennigan, to please get a picture or video. And God bless him he surely did, and I will be forever indebted to him for it.

Michael Fassbender was great craic and we did our own infamous version of the song, all in good jest. The crowd went wild. I was delighted to have this giant of the silver screen on stage with me. What a night! What a crowd!

I was in Heaven after the gig. I was having a great night, I didn't want it to end, but all good things must come to an end, or so I thought. I never could have envisioned what was to come next.

I was staying in the Cahernane Hotel that night, so after it was all finished and I got everything taken down, I made my weary journey back to the hotel. It was 4.00am. I was so tired at this stage, but I didn't care because of what had just happened earlier. Before I went to bed, I put the video up on You-tube and Facebook saying what an amazing night I had, and off I went to sleep.

I woke up at roughly 9.00am. It's an affliction I have, I cannot sleep in, ever. As I always do each morning, I checked my social media accounts and this morning I also checked You-tube. I nearly fell out of the bed, with what I saw. There were 3,000 views on You-tube alone. My Facebook page had started to blow up with likes, shares, and well wishes from friends. It was crazy!

My Gmail account went wild with media agencies looking to seek permission to put the footage up on their social media platforms and websites. Take into consideration this is what I woke to after a dodgy, broken five hour, sleep. But I replied to as many as I could.

I was totally overwhelmed by it all but in an incredible way. After all this excitement, I had the standard, hearty Irish breakfast, as I had a long drive ahead of me. I went back for a snooze.

I set off on my voyage home a few hours later, but the journey definitely took an extra two hours. I had to keep stopping the car to answer emails from media agencies as well as texts from friends and family. It was a crazy day altogether and that continued into the following night and day on the Sunday of the weekend.

I went out for a meal with my family in one of the local restaurants where I live in Ratoath, and before I reached the table in the restaurant, I got stopped about 15 times by people wishing me well and asking me about it.

I would be lying if I said I wasn't enjoying the attention, plus I knew by the Monday it would be old news. I enjoyed it while it lasted. The video clip was then repeated on television on many shows, including Irish fashion and showbiz programme *Xposé,* over the following weeks, so I was still getting texts and calls when this happened. It was a whirlwind experience to say the least.

Chapter 16

'You could have lost the arm.'

I mentioned earlier that I had to get a fistula into my arm for dialysis, which is basically a vein and an artery fused together. It's where the nurses insert the dialysis needles to cleanse your blood during your sessions. There are other methods, but this is the one I chose for my type of dialysis.

Anyway, most times after dialysis the medical staff will leave it in your arm, as it was doing no harm and God forbid, if any complications occur after transplantation, its means they don't have to insert it again.

It's quite unsightly and you are left with large lumps in your forearm and bicep area, but it's a small price to pay for a new life.

In April 2015, something wholly unexpected happened. It was just another normal week and a good one. The six piece band that I had at the time, In Full Swing, had been chosen to play at the National Food Awards, a large gala ceremony in the beautiful Mount Wolseley Hotel Spa and Golf Resort in Tullow, Co. Carlow.

At the time I was managing a busy print and design shop in Portmarnock in Dublin and that particular day, I didn't feel great. Of course I brushed it off like most men do.

I kept getting these strange pains in the tips of my fingers all day, and generally felt very lethargic and quite sick, but I put it down to being run-down or the onset of a flu.

I had arranged to get off early that day to prepare myself for that evening, but instead I went home and jumped into bed until I had to get up to get shower for the gig. There was an hour and half worth of a drive ahead of the band and I to get to the venue, so I needed the rest.

Eventually, we all arrived at the hotel and as per usual with most gigs, there is always a lot of waiting around.

While I was waiting with the lads to go on, I had two large Americano coffees to combat the fatigue but it barely woke me up. I was very pale. One of the lads commented saying I was a white as a ghost.

The arm that the fistula was in had started to pain me badly on the way down, but I ignored it, as I had work to do, playing to an audience of 400 plus people. 'The show must go on', as the saying goes.

After a lot of waiting around, it was time to hit the stage. I gathered myself and put my game face on even though I was in pain and felt quite disorientated. I was the singer and front man of the band, there was no backing out for me.

We kicked off with our usual up-tempo swing set and even though I felt absolutely dire, I got into the swing of it, excuse the pun.

About 12 songs in, I got an unmerciful pain in my left arm (fistula arm), and it completely seized up. I thought I was having a heart attack. The pain was like no pain I have ever felt before but there was an audience watching the band, so I tried my best to hide it.

I had no choice but to go on with the show, even if the pain was unbearable. God only knows how I carried on for another 16 songs, but I did.

It was coming up to half-time and as always, we would take a break at this point in the show. The pain had gotten a lot worse.

The moment came and I announced, 'Ladies and gentlemen, we are going to take a small break, please excuse us and we will be back to you in a little while.'

I walked off the stage in a professional manner, trying not to show the sheer agony I was in, and as I walked through a side door next to the stage, I just collapsed on the floor much to the bemusement and shock of my fellow band-mates. They were at a loss as to what to do, but I knew there was something seriously wrong.

I kept screaming in pain, asking anyone if they had painkillers and wondering how we would end the gig. It had been booked through an event company and I was the point of contact. Even in excrutiating pain, I still wanted to remain professional.

It's actually a bit of a blur to be honest, but thanks to the hard work and quick thinking of our guitarist at the time and the rest of the band, the gig went on as planned, without me.

I, on the other hand was laid out on a couch with the events team and manager of the hotel, screaming in pain, waiting on an ambulance, but the only hospital on call that night near to the hotel was Kilkenny hospital.

Eventually, the ambulance arrived and I was carried out on a stretcher by the paramedics. There was a wait of another 20 mins or so, as they were trying to stabilise me and my pain.

I was wearing a tuxedo for the gig that night and the paramedics had to rip my shirt arms off to apply a drip and attach a blood pressure monitor. I was given a painkiller of some description that took the sting out of the pain but it was still unbearable.

The journey to Kilkenny hospital took around 45 mins but felt like three hours. The paramedics were brilliant through it all, keeping me sane and stabilised and looking after me. Thank you so much to those who looked after me that night.

Through all this, Jennie hadn't heard from me, but I got someone to ring her and let her know. She was up the walls. She had no idea what was going on, that I was now in Kilkenny hospital waiting to be seen. My own phone had died and it was radio silence on my end. God bless her.

I was eventually seen by a doctor at around 1.00am. At this stage, they really didn't know what was going on, they just knew I was in really bad pain. I was still wearing the tuxedo from the night before with one sleeve completely ripped off and my bow tie untied. I must have looked like something out of a disaster or zombie movie.

I was lying up on a trolley for what seemed like an eternity, with people rushing around me. It was a really busy night in the A&E department, much to my dismay I can tell you.

The doctors eventually gave some form of drugs that again, dulled the pain somewhat. I was also able to doze in and out of consciousness with strange dreams that ensued, which were interesting, I can't remember what they were about, unfortunately. I was a lot more comfortable than before, but the pain was still there gnawing away at me and I still didn't know what was wrong. I had no feeling in my left arm and it had turned an unusual blue colour.

As you can imagine I was very worried.

At about 3.00am, I was moved onto another trolley in a cubicle and I was given more meds. I requested a sleeping tablet to help me sleep, which eventually did it's job and I drifted off.

As any transplant recipient or people on the transplant waiting list, or indeed any long term patient will know, the records of your medical history, out-patient visits and check-ups are all kept in the hospital you attend. This was Beaumont Hospital in my case and all I was afraid of was being kept down in Killkenny Hospital. They knew nothing about me or my history and it was so far from home. They only knew what I was telling them, but other than that, I was just some guy that was brought in the night before.

When I woke from my slumber I started to request a transfer to Beaumont Hospital,. I was so adamant in my request that I could see it was beginning to annoy the doctor overseeing my care, but it was the only way I would get the results badly needed. There was still no diagnosis of my condition and at this stage, I was shocked, confused, and still in terrible pain.

After a lot of words exchanged, some maybe a little rude, it was decided that I would be transferred to Beaumont Hospital later that morning.

We started to make the trek all the way back to Dublin. Thankfully, I was on very strong painkillers and the journey was a lot better than the one from Tullow to Kilkenny the night before.

I was admitted and pretty much got a bed straight away. I had lost a lot of feeling in my left arm. Of course, I knew something was wrong, but I didn't think it was anything that serious. The doctors were very concerned and started doing test after test that very day. They put me on various drips and they kept a very watchful eye on my condition. My first night they checked on me every 30 minutes, which I found quite alarming but still nobody was saying anything.

It was decided it had nothing to do with any renal difficulties and it was down to vascular issues, which is related to your veins and circulation. This was a whole different ball game completely. That's when I started to become extremely concerned. The pain had lessened but not a great deal. Worryingly, the feeling more or less had gone in my lower arm. The vascular team were then brought in to assess the situation.

After a lot of tests, the diagnosis was, that I had a burst blood clot in my left arm and that I was very lucky it didn't travel to my heart, because if it had, it would have been a very different scenario. It seemed to have been brought on by my fistula from the dialysis.

The decision was made to get me down to theatre and tie off the fistula, making it null and void, and it could not be used again but as I was out of dialysis, it was ok.

Through all of the ordeal, I don't think I had really comprehended how very serious this all was. I was just taking each day as it came. Day by day, I was slowly getting better, and the doctors and nurses were keeping a good eye on me and my levels.

I will never forget the afternoon my own doctor, Declan De Freitas came into me to have a chat. We were generally chit-chatting about everything, including the last few days, when mid-conversation he uttered the line as cool as you like, 'You could have lost the arm.'

I think I was having a cup of tea at the time when he came out with this revelation and I spat it out all over the bed sheets. I couldn't believe how cool he was talking about the possibility that I could have lost my left arm through amputation.

He was telling me the hard truth though, that if my circulation and feeling had not come back, it would have been amputated. I started blaming myself for overdoing it in the gym but there was nothing I had been doing my life to cause it.

After a few days of monitoring me and making sure the feeling had come back in my left arm and hand, and

143

all my levels had returned to normal, I was allowed leave the hospital to go home to my family. What a crazy few days it had been.

It was only when I got home it hit me how serious it all was but again, my positive mental attitude had helped to get me through it. Although, I had cried many times, mostly tears of joy, deep down I realised how very close I had come to losing my arm but my way of getting through this bad situation and any difficult situation in my life was to try to always concentrate on the positive things I have in my life and to think of how much they bring me joy.

It's a testament to the fact that no matter how well you think you are, you can always experience setbacks but knowing you have the strength to handle these setbacks and the fall out after them when they do occur.

Chapter 17

Health, fitness and mental health

Receiving organ donation from a deceased donor is, in my opinion, is one of the most amazing selfless acts that anyone can bestow on someone else. But the preservation and maintenance of the organ is your responsibility, much like having a baby. You have to make sure you take your meds on time, drink a lot of water, and eat right, along with many other things.

It can be very overwhelming at the start when you first undergo transplantation but if you set yourself a routine and stick to it, it makes it easier. It's important to make it a part of your lifestyle and not a chore. Fitness and leading a healthy life is one of the most vital things that anybody with a long term illness has to do.

After a tough Muay Thai class, with my trainer Aaron Browne

Your diet is a huge part of this. The way you lead your life has a huge impact on the longevity and health of your kidney. Sacrifices have to be made.

It took me a few years to get into my routine but now I lead a very healthy lifestyle with three to four gym visits a week. I also enjoy non-contact boxing and non-contact Muay Thai kick-boxing classes. For me, the benefits are insurmountable. From a psychological perspective, I find it extremely advantageous for relieving stress and giving me piece of mind. A bonus part of the whole thing is losing weight and staying in shape.

I was always a chubby kid growing up and then as a teenager the same. I got into the gym about 17 years ago, but I always just thought I knew it all. I most definitely didn't and unless I looked after myself now, I would still be prone to lash the weight on. It's in my family to put on weight, even by just looking at food. In my mind, I will always be a heavier person in a skinnier person's body.

Nowadays, I try really hard to follow a healthy diet, but if I want to go for a pint or enjoy a chocolate bar, I don't deny myself. After many, many years, I have finally cracked the diet end of things, I think.

I started to take up jogging four years ago in the gym and I set myself a goal to do 5K with each gym session. I did it and enjoyed it immensely.

The jogging training enabled me to jog/walk my first 5K in Corkagh Park for the *Run for a Life* in 2017. It was an amazing day where people came out in force, a lot of them past and new transplant recipients. I felt so proud to be part of such an amazing, unique group of people all with the same goal, all connected through the same reason.

The reason I wanted to write about this is because I wanted to let people know how much of a full life you can lead after transplantation and the things that you can achieve.

My advice to people is if there was ever one thing that you always wanted to do in your life, jump out of a plane, run a marathon, learn a language, etc... Just go for it. Nothing ventured, nothing gained, as the saying goes.

I do find nowadays that I suffer with injuries easier, my knees suffer, my feet can pain if I do too much on the treadmill, but I listen to my body (well most of the time), and I relax and chill for a few days or I find an alternative exercise I can do.

Earlier in the book, I spoke about getting the chance to sing at the 2010 World Transplant Games in The Helix Theatre in Dublin. I am, now, hopefully going to be on the other side competing. These amazing group of guys go and compete in different sports in different host cities each year. I am going to join Transplant Team Ireland. As I type this in 2021, the games were held virtually due to the Covid-19 global pandemic.

One of the first people I spoke to in Beaumont Hospital, who had a lot of experience in transplantation and in general, was a lovely man called Harry Ward. He is still going strong today and is the captain of Transplant Team Ireland. This man is a living legend.

Harry Ward, a true gent

When I bumped into him many years ago, I was only starting my whole kidney journey. He relaxed me with his reassuring words and I feel honoured to know him. Harry, keep on being the gent you are sir.

Transplant Team Ireland, 2017

Transplant Team Ireland competed in the games in 2017 and brought home an astounding tally of 32 Medals, including 14 gold, 7 silver, and 11 bronze.

All of these people have experienced chronic kidney or organ failure at one point in their lives and they have overcome all of the odds to be able to achieve these amazing feats. That's why when I penned the song for the games, I gave it the name 'Anything is Possible'.

One of the goals I have set myself for the foreseeable future is to be part of this amazing team of people.

I also have another goal that I want to achieve before I get too old. At 46 now, I can feel the age creeping in. No, I'm just kidding! I feel 21 again to be honest with the energy I possess.

I have decided in 2023 to take on another goal and that is to hopefully become a qualified fitness instructor and personal trainer with a move to sports nutrition.

I have such a huge interest in health and fitness that I want to learn everything there is to know and then, hopefully pass on my knowledge to other people, especially in the transplant community.

I haven't decided exactly who to do with it but I will be keeping a blog and a journal on my all my social media platforms at the time.

I am very excited about the future to be quite honest. I have learned now from experience that if you want something bad enough, you have to make it happen.

Nothing comes to you in this life, you have to work for it.

Nowadays, there is a lot of emphasis on mental health and feeling comfortable enough to open up. Unfortunately, there seems to still be a stigma attached to mental health, which is quite sad. A high percentage of people are afraid to speak out and talk to someone and a lot of times it leads to suicide as they feel there is nowhere to turn. I genuinely want to help people, to help them build their future with a positive mindset and outlook.

There shouldn't be any stigma around mental health whatsoever, and I for one, like many others have experienced these mixed emotions and dark days. When you are diagnosed with a chronic illness, you feel like you have no idea when or even if you will see a light at the end of the tunnel, and it becomes an endless road of treatment and hospital visits. In my case, dialysis three nights a week, four hours a session. The way I chose to deal with it was by concentrating on the good things in my life. I try to apply a positive mental attitude as much as possible. It most definitely got me through the whole process. I guess my own personal process is simple, in that, I clear my mind of anything negative and I concentrate on only good things, like my family, friends and activities that I enjoy.

I still to this day keep this attitude and it works for me. I always look to the future with positivity. I'm very sure my positivity and happy demeanour annoys the hell out of people on my social media accounts, but I constantly motivate myself and hopefully, I motivate some other people too on a daily basis.

Even though 99.5% of my hospital check-up appointments are absolutely fine with my levels all spot on, I still get nervous after my bloods are done. There is always that moment of dread before I get the level results on check-up days but keeping a healthy lifestyle and positive mindset gives me the reassurance that things will most likely be okay. Staying healthy benefits both your mental and physical health, so I try to implement this approach everyday.

I hope to bring my new knowledge of fitness, nutrition and keeping healthy in both mind and body to people in the transplant community that may feel that they are not able, or they believe that they can't lead a healthy life, as they feel they might injure themselves or their organ.

It will also be a service to anyone that wants to just talk about how their feeling, good or bad, as we all need someone to talk to. It will be for everyone across the board in the hopes that I can transform people's lives for the better because of the incredible gift of life and second chance I have been given.

I strongly believe that exercise and positivity have saved me from letting any dark days or mixed emotions cloud my judgement and decisions.

Earlier in this chapter I spoke about first my 5K. I really enjoy doing charity walks and runs. The photos on the next page show a selection of many of the walks and runs I have done.

It will always be a long road and I will be on my kidney medication for life, nearly 24 tablets per day, but it is a small price to pay for the wonderful life that I have now.

After my first 5K in 2017. Run for a Life, in aid of the Irish Kidney Association, took place in Corkagh Park

After completing my first charity 10K on St Stephen's morning, 2019

After completing 100K for Aoibheann's Pink Tie during lockdown in June, 2020

After completing my first virtual 10K for the Pigsback Run, in aid of the Marie Keating Foundation, during lockdown in October, 2020

After completing my second 10K for the Pigsback Run, in aid of the Marie Keating Foundation, in October, 2021

Chapter 18

My donor and saviour in Heaven

Throughout this book I have spoken of all the special people in my life, my family, friends, doctors and many more but imagine one person that you have never met or never will, being one of the most special people in your life. Sounds funny doesn't it?

Well, only for this one very special person and their beautiful and selfless act of donating their organs, would I be in the amazing position of being able to look to the future and plan goals that I want to achieve, and what a position it is to be in.

My kidney donor unfortunately lost their life on December 29th, 2007. In turn through their selfless act, blessed me with a brand new life.

I will probably never know who this wonderful angel is. That's the only name I have for them and it fits them perfectly, for anyone who decides to help others by carrying an organ donor card is an angel. It's a wonderful act of kindness and a lot of people have helped not one, but a number of people by deciding to donate their organs. It is truly amazing.

There is a kind of unspoken rule that you don't get a chance to contact or meet the donor's family, but hopefully someday, by the grace of God, I will meet them or even get a chance to write to them to let them know how much their loved one's act of kindness has helped me since that fateful day in 2007.

I honestly believe that some of my donors trait's have lived on in me. Some people say it's an old wives, tale, but I honestly believe it. I have always had drive and ambition but nothing like now. They must have been an amazing person when they were alive.

Some people do not how lucky they are and they don't look after and often abuse the organ that is donated to them. There have been many stories of this, including famous people.

These people ultimately pay the price in the end, but I find it very disrespectful that people that are lucky enough to receive an organ don't have the respect and show downright bad manners toward the new organ they have received.

The doctors said to me after the operation, 'You must treat the new kidney like a new baby, you wouldn't abuse a baby in any way so why would you do it to an organ'

Be it a kidney, liver, lung, heart, etc you should always look after it everyday.

I would love to meet the family of my donor one day. I don't think it's allowed, but I am going to look into maybe writing to them anonymously, if that's possible to say how grateful I am to them for my second chance at life and how I have made sure that I have honoured my donor by looking after my transplanted organ with exercise, healthy eating, etc.

I am making a plea to everyone that is reading this to go out and get a organ donor card. You can even do it online now too.

You never know when you may need it yourself if the unthinkable happens.

You can request the organ donor card from the Irish Kidney Association at:

https://ika.ie/get-a-donor-card/

Chapter 19

My fifteen minutes of TV fame

Ever since my operation I had always wanted to talk about my kidney journey and subsequent transplant story. I wanted to spread my positive message in any way I could, and what better way to do it than on TV.

I had done many radio interviews, but I wanted to go further, as I felt it was a story that needed to be told. Millions of people have dialysis, renal failure and kidney transplants every year but what matters most is what you do with your life after transplantation and how you deal with such a big change, emotionally and physically.

My friend, Luke Thomas, was a regular panellist on *The Elaine Show,* hosted by Elaine Crowley on Virgin Media Television and I had mentioned it to him a few times, asking him how I would go about it, and he gave my all the advice he could.

I decided to email the show and give a brief overview of my story. Low and behold, the lovely researcher gave me a call and asked me a few questions. To my utter delight, the researcher then asked would I be ok to come in the following Monday. I couldn't believe it, I was finally getting my chance to tell my story on daytime TV.

I didn't know what to expect and I had to pick Luke's brain about TV interview techniques. I am a chatterbox and I have a terrible habit of talking over people when I

160

am feeling nervous. As he was on most weeks, I knew that he would be more versed on it than I.

The lovely panel on *The Elaine Show*. Left to right: Sally-Anne Clarke, Rachel Ryan, and Sue Jordan

Luke told to me to just relax and wait until the interviewer finished speaking before answering any questions. I took his advice and engraved that into my brain.

I remember getting up the morning of the interview and going for a run. I heard the camera adds 10 pounds, so I wanted to feel as good as I could on TV, very shallow I know, but I was only getting one shot at this.

I didn't know who was on the panel that day. I arrived at Virgin Media Studios in Ballymount racked with nerves. I was led to the green room. The other guests began to filter in and they all introduced themselves to me which made me feel at ease. I explained why I was there and what I would be talking about.

The guests on the panel were L'Ecrivain Restaurateur, Sally-Anne Clarke, Presenter and Producer on Dublin's 98FM, Rachael Ryan, Blogger, Sue Jordan, and the wonderful Agony Aunt Tina Koumarianos, who was such an intriguing person.

I was coming on as a special guest to tell my story, but I had to wait until the first part of the show was covered. That added to my anxiety and nervousness but the lovely Tina Koumarianos made me feel very at ease.

They broke for a commercial break and it was now time for me to go on, ahhhhhhhhh! I was screaming inside but still very excited. Ruth announced me on with an introduction that I didn't feel worthy of, as it was so amazing, but I came on, sat down, took a big deep breath and told myself in my head to just enjoy it.

When I chilled out, it was so enjoyable. It was like chatting to friends and because it's a subject that I know a lot about, it was easy to talk about it.

I talked about my illness in detail from the very start with renal failure to undergoing dialysis and the subsequent transplant that I received. I spoke of how lucky I felt at getting a second chance at life. It was very therapeutic to lay it all out for everyone to hear, and I felt a great sense of relief.

Ruth Scott and I in deep conversation.
What a lovely person Ruth is.

We touched on how fitness had become my saviour and still is to this day with my daily fitness regiment. We spoke about my upcoming Sinatra inspired show, in the Draíocht theatre, in Blanchardstown. Ruth was even so kind as to give it a plug for me. Thank you dearly, to Ruth, for that. We also spoke of my past years in the music business and the venues I had played abroad and up and down the country.

The one thing that all the ladies on the panel wanted to hear about was my dalliance and duet with A-list star, Michael Fassbender, in The Europe Hotel in Killarney and the viral video that followed. They were extremely interested in that one. I wonder why!

Sitting alongside presenter and DJ, Ruth Scott. The panel made me feel so welcome and at ease that day.

Ruth showed the video and the girls all swooned... at Mr Fassbender, of course.

I felt very natural on TV and actually didn't find it intimidating. All my worry and anxiety was in vain. The general feedback from people was the same, that I came across very natural, which was good to hear. It's something I would love to explore further, in acting or presenting of some sort. Maybe you will see me on *The Late Late Show* some day. Or even presenting my own show.

Chapter 20

From dialysis to the Draíocht

'Vision without action is merely a dream. Action without vision just passes the time. Vision with action can change the world.'

This is a quote by Joel Barker and it is very true in many ways. A lot of people speak about dreams and aspirations but never actually do anything to bring them to fruition and then regret it for the rest of their lives.

One dream of mine, after my operation and the amazing journey I have been on, was to write a book to tell my story. Here we are now, I have fulfilled that dream and I will have this book to look back on and be proud of, for the rest of my life.

In a previous chapter, I spoke about another dream I had, which was to have my own headliner show in a theatre with a big swing band, special guests and hopefully if I could make it happen, a large gospel choir.

That very dream came true on May 31st, 2018, when I staged my first theatre show in the fantastic Draíocht theatre in Blanchardstown, Dublin.

I had thought about it many times previously but got too scared at the idea and the risk I would be taking if the show didn't sell. Then, the subsequent embarrassment that would have followed could have spelled the end of any further dreams I had, as my confidence would have been knocked for six too.

There was a lot to take on board by putting a production like this together, from cost, marketing, band selection, song selection and getting musical charts arranged for the different songs, guest selection and most of all, promotion and how I would sell it to make it all a success.

After a few encouraging words and a push from Luke Thomas I decided to look into it and see what it would take. Luke, at this point in his career, had put on a few theatre shows with his band, so I thought he would be the best man to ask. He helped me immensely with information about the ins and outs of staging a show.

I contacted a promoter who I had been keeping an eye on professionally, from afar, with the different shows he was putting on. He seemed to be having success, so I thought why not. We had a great initial meeting and I was very excited by it all, after he explained how it all worked with the theatres.

We started the process and everything was going well, negotiations wise, then, all of a sudden, he went cold and completely blanked me. That was a setback I didn't need and I was a little confused as to why he did it. After a few days of soul searching and a few calls with Luke, I decided to go it alone and do it all on my own, which I knew would be hard.

Firstly, I had to come up with a concept for the show. I have always been a huge Frank Sinatra fan since I started on my musical journey. I still listen to him on a daily basis, I love the tone of his voice and the effortless speech-level singing he was known for so after a lot of thought, I came up with the concept. ***Sinatra – Nothing but the Best:*** *A celebration of the music and life of Frank Sinatra and the many other artists that shaped the Swing music era.*

Secondly, I contacted the Draíocht theatre and enquired about dates that were suitable. Back and forth we went and eventually, we decided on Thursday night, May 31st, 2018. I was wary of having it on a Thursday, but I was given wise words by someone who said my target market was an older demographic, retired people and genuine swing music fans, so that settled my mind a little.

Now that the date and concept had been decided, next up was to look for top musicians that would do this timeless music justice and I set off on my quest to get the best in Dublin. Thankfully, over the years I have struck up friendships with great musicians that are masters of the craft. Getting them on board was going to be tricky but I was determined.

I had to call on everyone I knew in the music business and get the best of the best. In the end I did just that and then some. I could not have had better musicians on my debut show, they were just perfect.

I picked all the songs for the show and the particular arrangements, so now, I had to find the best arranger out there to do these songs justice. I wasn't sure if this was the only theatre show I would ever do and I wanted it to be as perfect as I could.

I had heard this certain guy's name spoken of fondly in the area of musical arrangements and composing and how good he was. I never thought for one minute that I would get him to do the arrangments for my show. His name is Dave McGauran and what a complete gentleman and genius this guy is.

Between the jigs and the reels, and many emails back and forth, we started the process. He was very understanding with my whims and ideas, and the particular arrangements I had picked. I am a perfectionist at the best of times, so I can be a bit of a pain, but he was brilliant and unbelievably professional and honest, which is what was needed, especially from someone like Dave who knows the business inside out.

In the background, the ticket sales process had begun. Thankfully, my digital marketing and social media diploma was put to good use, and I used Facebook and

169

Instagram to set up marketing campaigns to sell tickets to the show.

The staff in Draíocht were amazing and so easy to deal with. With my daily and weekly emails asking this question and that, they never once got frustrated with me. Well, to my face anyway.

All along, through out the process, I was riddled with anxiety wondering would the tickets sell. Could I make the show the success I wanted it to be? If it didn't sell, how would I recover from the embarrassment? The financial risk was rummaging around in my head.

It was so much to take on, but I had a good chat with myself one day and I said, 'You can do this, you're well able.'

The few months were a whirlwind of emails, texts, phone calls to musicians, arrangers, asking friends for advice and encouragement, and most of all, the brilliant staff in Draíocht. How they didn't kill me and let me back for a second show, I will never know.

The tickets were selling really well, and I was pinching myself, but I needed to get to a certain amount of ticket sales so that everyone on the show was paid and looked after, from the theatre, the sound and lighting crew, singers and musicians to the photographer on the night.

It was time to pick special guests and hopefully, secure the amazing talent of a gospel choir. I had people in mind and it was just a case of securing their services to bring that extra element of class to the show. This was no longer a show but a dream unfolding, and the biggest production of my life.

Another whirlwind of meetings, emails, texts and phone calls ensued. I then secured the services of four fantastic special guests and a 12 piece choir called United Harmony. I was over the moon, as I could see the vision forming that I had for it.

Ticket sales continued to rocket, much to my shock but secret delight, and then I finally reached the ticket amount that I needed to get to. This meant I had no worries about anyone getting paid and I wouldn't owe any money to the theatre, as that was covered.

Next to happen was rehearsals. I had finalised all the arrangements with the composer, Dave McGauran. It was time to get to work on creating and doing this timeless music justice with some of the top musicians in the country.

It was so exciting to see and hear all the different arrangements coming together in rehearsals with the big band, special guests and the amazing gospel choir. It added to my own excitement about my vision and dream coming to life... the sound of the brass section ringing through, the beautiful sound of the piano, the double bass and drums, keeping alive the wonderful rhythm of these fantastic songs from Frank Sinatra, Dean Martin, Michael Bublé, and many more.

Time was ticking by and everything was basically in place with only four weeks to go, when I got the greatest news... my debut headliner theatre show was SOLD OUT. There wasn't a ticket to be got for it. I remember getting the call. I was in total shock, mixed emotions of happiness, nervousness, all at the same time.

I had been on a special diet and gym training regime for the show, as I wanted to look my best in my suit under those bright stage, but I think I may have over done it at the time as coming up to it, people were asking me was I okay. I had dropped over 18 pounds in weight (roughly a stone and four pounds), weight I didn't really have to lose.

One of the special guests, Nikki, a good pal of mine, rang me concerned, asking if was my health okay, as I had dropped the weight. The ironic thing was, I had never felt fitter or healthier in my life.

With only two weeks to go, my butterflies grew bigger and bigger. I started to think, 'Have I everything done that I need to do?, 'Have I forgotten something?.

These are natural emotions for anyone doing this all their lives, but this was my very first time on this scale.

More emails and texts and phone calls ensued making sure that everybody was okay for the date and nobody had fallen ill that I needed to replace. Thankfully, everything was okay and my plan was going ahead.

Then it was time for final rehearsals, which we flew through, as everyone had gone off and made the changes they needed to their music charts. We had a great time that night. We played the whole show from start to finish and it sounded just wonderful. We all left that night in great form, really looking forward to the show.

I knew everything was going too well, and with just over a week to go, I got a very bad cold. I panicked straight away, as I was still working during the day. I would have preferred to get under the duvet and just hide away until I felt better, so I took advice from everyone, as to the best remedy to rid myself of this head cold and sniffles, and I put myself on voice rest and a voice diet of paracetemol, hot water, lemon, and fresh ginger.

If you know me, that was very hard. I never stop talking but it worked. Over the next few days, I could feel it clearing up and my voice returning and two days before the show it was back. I still rested the voice until the big day.

I had taken the day off before the show and the day of the show, as I knew I would running around like a headless chicken organising the last few bits.

Show day had come and I woke that morning with a sense of calm. I knew that feeling would soon change later as stage time drew closer. I made myself a coffee and planned my day out with what I had to do.

Then the errands began. I made sure not to run myself ragged. The emotions of excitement and nervousness would take it out of me during the day.

Load-in time into the theatre was 4.30pm onwards that day, so everyone had their info and what time to be there. After I had everything done, I went for a nap, funny as it may seem. I am a big fan of naps and even a 20-minute disco nap as I like to call it, sets me up.

We all started to arrive at the theatre at 4.30pm and from then, it was like someone hit a fast forward button. The band and I all got set up, and the special guests arrived at different times to rehearse their songs, all sounding great. I wanted to make sure that everything was just right.

I remember going up to the back of the theatre to take it all in and just chill for five minutes while the band worked away and the gospel choir rehearsed their part. The sense of pride just overwhelmed me. There were tears in my eyes, tears of joy, of course.

It took me back to the days of my renal failure when I was very sick. I wasn't sure how my life was going to turn out and how uncertain everything was, and now, here I was sitting in a beautiful theatre, watching my first sold out show unfold in front of me.

We had to finish up and get out of sight so that the audience could start to filter in. That is when the real nerves kicked in, but I had brought along some rescue remedy and a bottle of Jack Daniel's to sort the butterflies out.

Here I am, contemplating running out the back door of the theatre out of sheer nervousness. Thank God I didn't.

It's the weirdest feeling you get, in that hour before stage time. You have been running on auto-pilot up until then and then, all of sudden, there is a strange feeling of calm. It's hard to describe it. It's very strange indeed, I actually nearly collapsed and to be honest, I ended up getting sick. I jumped into a hot shower to freshen up and get my tuxedo on. It was like stepping into a different body, ready for action, like a soldier going into battle.

The audience were in their seats waiting for the show to start. The band were in the green room eating pizza and drinking beer I had bought them as a small thank you for getting me to this point.

We got the five minute curtain call for stage time, so the band made their way out onto the stage. I had those few minutes to myself. I prayed to God and my dad in Heaven to guide me, to look over me, and to please make the night a success.

The stage was set. This was just before the band arrived on stage.
My dad always plays a big part in my shows, keeping an eye on us all in Heaven.

The opening number on the night we had planned was the Rodgers and Hart classic, 'The Lady Is a Tramp', made famous by Frank Sinatra.

All roads had led to this. What a rush to come out that night and entertain the fantastic audience from start to finish, with the most amazing musicians on stage with me. I couldn't have done without them.

It's upbeat intro is one of the most recognised in this style and genre of music, and that was my cue to walk out on stage. I stuck my chest out, shoulders back, and proudly walked out on stage (even though I was racked with nerves inside) to the loudest applause I had ever heard. WOW, what a feeling... 'She gets too hungry, for dinner at eight'... the opening line, was met with cheers and whistles.

Act 1

The Lady Is a Tramp
Bad, Bad Leroy Brown
I Get a Kick Out of You
Come Fly With Me
Strangers in the Night
The Way You Look Tonight
Summer Wind
Smile
I've Got Rhythm

Act 2

Luck Be a Lady
You Make Me Feel so Young
The Best Is Yet to Come
Fly Me to the Moon
At Last
Mr Bojangles
Night and Day

Act 3

One for My Baby (And One More for the Road)
It Was a Very Good Year
Moon River
I've Got You Under My Skin
My Baby Just Cares for Me
Feeling Good
Haven't Met You Yet
Mack the Knife

Act 4

Ain't That a Kick in the Head
Little Ole Wine Drinker, Me
That's Amore
New York, New York
That's Life
My Way

The set list from the night

We followed up with the fantastic 'Bad, Bad Leroy Brown'. The crowd started to clap and sing along to the very well known chorus, which was brilliant and did a lot for my stage confidence. Straight from that song I blasted into the Michael Bublé arrangement of 'I Get a Kick Out of You' and then into the famous Sinatra standard, 'Come Fly With Me'... 'pack up, let's fly away.' The crowd cheered and clapped much to my delight.

My heart was beating double time and the nerves were still there, but they were good nerves fuelled by adrenalin.

On stage with Hannah Roddy performing the Nat King Cole classic 'Smile'. This girl is going to do great things.

It was time to call out my first guest, a wonderfully talented young lady by the name of Hannah Roddy. Hannah, who is only 19, has graced every theatre stage in the country, playing the lead character on many huge theatre productions. She has the most beautiful voice you have every heard.

I had picked out the Nat King Cole classic, 'Smile', that was written by the late and great Charlie Chaplin, as a duet for us. It's such a beautiful arrangement. Our voices complimented each other very well on the night and the crowd loved it. Hannah just shone for the super talented young lady she is. It was a pleasure to duet with her.

When we sang the duet, it was then time for Hannah to perform a solo song, She sang the Judy Garland classic, 'I Got Rhythm'. She had picked it herself and WOW, she brought the house down. The crowd stood and cheered for her in their seats, which was amazing and very well deserved.

I had to keep reminding myself time and time again, metaphorically, of how lucky I was to be on stage with all these amazing artists and musicians, playing to a sold out theatre. The feeling was surreal, song after song, the show just kept getting better and better with such classics as 'You Make Me Feel so Young' and 'The Best Is Yet to Come'.

My good pal, Nikki Kavanagh, and I, backstage in the green room.

The next special guest to come to the stage was the vocal powerhouse that is Nikki Kavanagh. Nikki is in the business many years and possesses a natural vocal talent that has to be heard to be believed. We have become really good friends over the years, and I was proud to get to sing with her on stage.

We duetted on the classic standard, 'Fly Me to the Moon'. It went down a storm, but her solo song took the crowd's breath away. She performed the Etta James classic, 'At Last'. Nikki did it the only way she knows how... outstandingly.

It was time for the interval and as tired as I was, I just wanted to keep going. The adrenalin and endorphins had well and truly kicked in. It was probably a good thing to break then. Judging by the rate I was going I probably would have collapsed, which for my debut show wouldn't have been great.

Mr Michael Fay and I opening the second part of the show.
I was privileged to have him as the pianist and
musical director on the show.

We opened up the second half of the show in a way and style I had seen many music stars who I love and admire do, where they sit beside their pianist and play a song with just vocals and piano. We opened up with 'One for My Baby (And One More for the Road)', a beautiful song and melody with just Michael Fay, my pianist and musical director on the show. This guy is a class act. I was was privileged to have him on the crew.

A great photo taken by brother, Niall Kirwan, the official photographer on the show, with my dad and Frank Sinatra overseeing proceedings.

The next song 'It Was a Very Good Year', another classic in Frank Sinatra's repertoire, was always a favourite of mine, but I never got a chance to sing it. I really wanted this song to be as atmospheric as it could be and I hoped to do it as much justice as I could. It was the one song that as much as I rehearsed it, I kept forgetting the lyrics for some reason, but on the night, I just relaxed, sat back and performed it word perfect. My mam gave me one of the best compliments I have ever been told me, that I sounded very like Frank Sinatra singing it, which was the ultimate compliment but then again, she is biased!

We then played the classic, 'Moon River', another song I had always wanted to perform on the big stage but never had the chance to and here I was living that dream, another pinch me moment. I actually got chills on stage singing this one. It sounds crazy but performing, to many artists, is like a drug and that night, the high I felt being on the big stage was the best feeling in the world.

Myself and Hazel Peters duetting on 'I've Got You Under My Skin'. We had such fun that night performing on stage together.

The next guest up on the night was a soulful songstress by the name of Hazel Peters. I have known Hazel for a few years from being on the circuit and we hailed from the same area years ago. I have always loved Hazel's vocals, as they are so natural and soulful and she have a great versatility in any genre.

We had such great fun duetting on the Cole Porter classic, 'I've Got You Under My Skin',. I came in late on the second verse and we both got the giggles. but as true professionals, we kept going. That has always been the main thing for me with singing. I always make sure to have fun when performing and not take myself too seriously.

When the cheering stopped from the crowd, I left the stage for Hazel to perform her solo number, the beautiful Nina Simone classic 'My Baby Just Cares for Me', and the crowd clapped along to her performance. I had picked this especially, as I knew Hazel would do a great version of it.

I followed up in the Nina Simone vein with the Michael Bublé version of her classic, 'Feeling Good', a favourite song and arrangement of mine. I was so hyped up from how well the show was going so far so I wanted to have fun with the crowd and have them sing it back to me. They didn't fail me one bit.

They really got into it and joined in on the Michael Bublé original, 'Haven't Met You Yet', and the absolutely golden and famous standard, 'Mack the Knife' where they joined me on the chorus.

The crowd singing along with me to 'Haven't Met You Yet'

Having over 250 people singing back to you on your own headline show is a feeling that quite frankly, I have found hard to top since. It is the best feeling in the world.

He is the Dean to my Frank and always will be

I knew we were coming into Act four of the show, the final part, but I just wanted it to go on and on. I knew that this part would be very special, as it was time to introduce one of my best friends on stage, Ireland's answer to Dean Martin, Mr. Joe Monks. I have known Joe about 11 years now, in a professional and personal capacity. This guy is one of the most multi-talented and humble people I have ever known.

We opened the final part of the show with the Dean Martin classic, 'Ain't That a Kick in the Head', where Joe walked out on stage to the intro and a very large applause from the crowd. Usually we would be whispering in each other's ear while the other was singing to try to distract one another and make one another laugh, but we knew we had to be professional on this night, well mostly professional.

We followed up with the singalong classic, 'Little Ole Wine Drinker, Me,' by Dean Martin and again, the crowd sang the whole song with us. Joe and I just kept laughing and smiling, as we were just enjoying ourselves, living our dream up there and just listening to the crowd singing back to us.

Joe and myself on stage entertaining the crowd

It was time for Joe's solo performance and his swan song, the famous Dean Martin classic, 'That's Amore'. I left the stage and let Joe work his magic on the crowd, I stood in the wings and watched his performance with an immense sense of pride as Joe just sung his heart out and had the crowd in the palm of his hands. It was an absolute pleasure to share the big stage with him. He deserved all the applause he got that night.

My fantastic band whipped the crowd into a frenzy when they started the intro of the big band classic, 'New York, New York'. Although dancing wasn't allowed, I encouraged everyone to stand up in their seats so, I could see them singing, dancing and waving their hands. Some of the floor staff turned a blind eye. I think they were enjoying themselves too much to care. It was a joy to see everyone having such a good time. I felt we had given them value for money and it wasn't over yet. The whole theatre sang along for this well known classic and all I could do was smile the biggest smile. We ended it with the huge crescendo finish that the song has. I briefly left the stage, while the band finished the outro of the song. I had a quick sip of Jack Daniel's in true Sinatra style, composed myself, took a few deep breaths, and I stepped back out to a still cheering crowd.

We were down to the last two songs of the night. I had dreamt of this moment all my life of what was to come next. I had always wanted to sing with a gospel choir on my own headline theatre show. I had gotten the chance to sing with a gospel choir eight years previous thankfully, but this was my ultimate dream on my own show.

Over the last few months, I had gotten in touch with a great pal of mine, Lisa McEvoy, and along with a group of lovely ladies, they formed The United Harmony Choir, especially for my show.

Standing alongside The United Harmony Choir

I visualised that I would be front and centre, flanked by this amazing choir of very talented ladies.

I introduced The United Harmony Choir on stage, again to rapturous applause. Eight very vocally talented ladies made up the choir, four on each side of me, led by my pal Lisa. We had led rehearsals the previous months about how it would sound and what way it would go, and it didn't disappoint. The band came in on the big intro we had rehearsed for the classic, 'That's Life', and I personally got this new surge of energy and felt every note of that intro. I sang the opening line, 'That's life', with the choir backing me with the same line as in the original and WOW, what a butterflies in the tummy moment. It was an unbelievable moment on that stage, and it just got better and better from there.

Since my dad died back in 2006, any gig that I played I always dedicated the final song of the show to him. This time was no different. The next and final song of the show was the classic that was written by a brilliant man called Paul Anka, but made famous by The Chairman of The Board, Frank Sinatra, the well known and powerful standard, 'My Way'. It's a very special song to my family, as it was my dad's favourite song. He sang it many times over the years at family occasions and he did an amazing version of it. He had the most powerful voice. This was by far the most poignant part of the show, and the thing

188

I was most afraid of was losing it and breaking down in tears. I can get very emotional singing it, as it reminds me so much of my dad.

My pianist and MD, Michael Fay, started playing the piano intro slowly, and I spoke to the crowd to tell the story about my dad passing and how important the song was to my family and I. I felt good, as I had my amazing band and The United Harmony Choir for moral support. I wanted these few moments and this song to the most special part of the show. Anyone who knows this fantastic timeless classic will know how the song builds and builds to a huge finish, and that's exactly what it did with the choir and I in full voice and the band bringing it up from the rear. I just wanted to freeze time and make this moment last forever. The euphoria I felt was out of this world and I think everyone there that night felt it too, which made it even better.

That last note of the song can be a tricky one, but I gave it my all, 'I did it my wayyyyyyyy. The band played on with the outro and we received a standing ovation from the crowd. My voice faltered on the last few words, 'Yes, it was my way'. The crowd still standing and clapping.

Deep down I was trying to hold in tears. I wanted to cry with joy, but I had to hold it together for just another few minutes.

189

I felt like the luckiest man in the world to stand on the stage with the crème de la crème of the music industry.

I called out the band and guests to the front of the stage for a bow, because without them, none of this would have ever been possible. Each and everyone of them were on this crazy journey with me right from the very start, and I was eternally grateful for all their hard work and dedication in making this the best show ever, without as much as a complaint, well to my face anyway.

These guys are some of the most respected musicians and singers and I felt so lucky to grace that stage with them that night. This was by far one of the best nights of my life.

I wake every morning now with a positive mind and I try to see the best in every situation. I know how far I have come and how lucky I have been in my life, physically and emotionally. I have been blessed in so many ways.

Chapter 21

My brush with Covid

As I write this chapter of the book, it is mid-December 2021. The world has been badly affected by the Covid-19 pandemic since March 2020, a respiratory illness that that spreads like wildfire and has caused many fatalities across the world. There has been global lockdowns, many businesses and industries have been decimated, there has been many variants of the virus, and everybody has had to wear masks and receive vaccinations to try quell the situation.

Due to my transplant, I am in the high risk category and in the last two years since the pandemic, I have had to limit my travel, contact with other people, and I have had to work from home, which ironically, was a good thing for me, as I got to spend more time with my family.

I thought I had done very well not to catch the virus and had been watching myself very carefully and making sure I got tested if I felt ill in any way. But, around the beginning of October, I managed to pick up a bad cold with a blocked nose and sore chest, so like before, I got tested, and my test came back negative.

This cold I had persisted and I had to get another test which again, came up negative. I found this odd, as I couldn't understand why the cold was persisting for so long.

It was coming up to Halloween on the 31st October and our neighbours and ourselves had organised a covid safe get together outside our houses for my daughter and her friends. On Halloween morning I woke up with the congestion that I had for the last 6 weeks, but I suggested we go for a nice walk on the beach, it was a beautiful sunny Sunday morning, as I found the fresh air made me feel a lot better. I actually felt great on the beach and jogged for most of it.

When we got home, I felt a little foggy and disorientated and ended taking a nap for a while. My neighbour called in and asked did I want to get some shopping for the Halloween get together, later that evening. I went reluctantly, as I had started to feel quite ill. It was a different feeling to anything I had experienced before but as I had tested negative twice I honestly didn't think it was Covid-19.

Ironically, something that Halloween morning, subconsciously told me to book another test for that Monday, November 1st. Covid-19 test results in Ireland take from up to 24 to 48 hours to come back to you.

As Halloween evening drew on, I started to feel more disorientated but I put on a brave face for my daughter and tried to enjoy the night but deep down I knew there was something wrong. I woke up the following morning still feeling congested but with that horrible foggy feeling.

My worst fears were confirmed when I received the text from the HSE (Health Service Executive), who carry out the tests. I had tested positive for Covid-19. The criteria was, on receiving a positive test result, you must isolate in a room in your house away from your family or other occupants, so as not spread the virus.

I started my isolation and felt relatively okay. I looked forward to the date when I was out of the isolation period to get things back to normal, or so I thought. My symptoms worsened tenfold over the next few days, from crippling headaches and fever to severe loss of appetite. The strangest symptom was when I lost my sense of taste and smell. Due to my severe lack of appetite and the headaches causing me to sleep up to between 16 and 18 hours a day, I dropped nearly 7kg in weight in a very short space of time. This in turn made me feel very weak. I lost all coordination in my legs and even walking to the toilet seemed like a mammoth task.

This all happened very quickly, but I was so out of it, I could barely grasp what was going on. It was now the Wednesday of the following week, my proposed day to be out of isolation. My wife begged me to get an ambulance. I felt too weak. I promised her I would get one the following day. I only seemed to be getting worse by the day. My family was very worried as was I, not just about the Covid-19 sickness I was experiencing but also my kidney health, as I was severely dehydrated and that is extremely dangerous for a transplanted kidney's health.

This particular night was probably the worst I had experienced so far, symptoms wise, so the fact that we were calling an ambulance the following day was the best decision by far.

The following day came after a horrible night, and I was ready to go to hospital. I felt so weak and ill. The ambulance came and the paramedic assessed me in the house first and had to help me out to the awaiting vehicle. The journey only took about 20 mins to Beaumont Hospital, but it seemed so much longer.

We arrived at the A&E entrance and I was brought in on stretcher to an area where they assessed you. They put me on oxygen straight away, took my bloods, blood pressure and my temperature. It had been rising to high levels right since I contracted the virus, hence the fevers and crippling headaches. The hospital was overrun at the time and have been for some time with the pandemic. I honestly had resigned myself to the fact that I would be on the trolley I was on for all of my recovery in hospital, but after a few hours they informed me I would be going to a Covid ward. Even in my unwell, weakened state, I was happy to hear this.

The photo that worried a lot of people, just after I arrived in the hospital

I got moved to the ward, which at that time had no one in it except myself. During a very sleepless first night in hospital, two more people got moved into the ward in the early hours.

The nurses were monitoring my health from the time I arrived, taking my bloods, and checking blood pressure and my temperature at all hours to keep an eye on me. I seemed to be getting more unwell by the day, my temperature was rising to scary levels, and the nurses were very concerned.

I was administered intravenous antibiotics and steroids too, but I honestly didn't care what they gave me at that stage as long as it made me better. I was taking oxygen 24 hours through the nose, as my lungs were compromised due to the virus. I had also developed a consistent dry cough that caused me to dry retch a lot, which I hated.

My temperature kept rising over the next few days and at this stage, the doctors had been in with me to assess my situation and decide on the best course of action.

I was fighting two battles. My kidney creatinine level, which is a very important level in the health and safety of

196

kidneys, especially transplanted organs, had risen to 300 from my baseline level. This would usually be around 115. The doctors and I needed to get this back down. My body had basically dried out when I was recovering at home, and I unintentionally dehydrated my kidney.

The Covid ward had filled up at this stage, and with the collection of different people, it made the days more bearable, as we all tried to help one another mentally, through this horrible journey we were on with the Covid-19 virus, by chatting and sharing stories, I became nearly institutionalised with the groundhog day aspect of being there. My meals arriving at the same time each day, the nurses coming to check your vital statistics at the same time each day too. I read quite a lot when I wasnt feeling so ill. It was all a coping mechanism for me to get through this and it definitely helped me.

My temperature reached its highest at 41 degrees celsius and that was probably my worst night in hospital. It was one of the scariest times of my life as the nurses and doctors tried to get it down by increasing my antiobiotics and other medications.

The following day, which was a Wednesday, my kidney doctor came in and told me that I would be there for another seven to 10 days. He was extremely concerned about my high temperature readings. At that stage, I had already been there over a week or so. It was hard to judge,

The days just ran into each other. I was so disappointed with this news. I was missing my family and it was quite lonely in hospital but I understood my doctor's thinking. The reason why I noted the day was because my daughter, Amelia, had given me a get well soon card. On the card, she wrote a message saying that she would love me to be home for the Late Late Toy Show, the Friday of the following week, which in Ireland is a national institution. It's a toy show on a long-running Irish chat show that happens every year, and parents allow their children to stay up later to watch it.

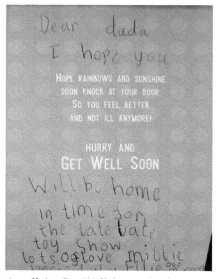

Amelia's, Get Well Soon, Card that spurred me on to fight harder against the virus

I knew from that day, I had to get better. That little card from Amelia changed my mindset and made me fight this virus just that little bit harder. My whole demeanour changed. I put the prospect of another seven to 10 days to the back of my mind. Instead, I channelled it into getting home to watch the Late Late Toy Show with my family. I had started to try to get up and move around more, by doing ten to fifteen laps of the ward each day. I started to breathe on my own more each day without using the oxygen. This helped my positivity and I felt better within myself.

I'm not a hugely religious person, in the sense of attending mass each week, but I do pray to God and my dad each night, and I prayed every night in hospital to get better and to just get home. But, whatever happened over the next few days, my temperature began to drop to better levels. I'm not sure whether it was divine intervention, but I was delighted in any case.

Finally starting to feel better and able to smile again

The weekend came and I was in much better form. Things were finally starting to improve and I could see some light at the end of this tunnel.

The medical staff were much happier too, as I was eating better also, which was helping my strength to fight the virus. My temperature continued to drop right through the weekend. I was still quite underweight, but I was glad to be able to eat properly again. I didn't want to tempt fate by getting excited about going home. They were starting to let people in the ward go home that felt better, so I just resigned myself to the prospect of going home at the end of the following week as discussed with my doctor.

I filled up my remaining time with reading, taking notes for this book, my new light exercise regime of walking the ward, and catching up on my favourite series on Netflix and Now TV.

It was Sunday night and before I turned my light off and put my head on my pillow, I prayed that the new week would bring something good. I prayed that I would get home as healthy as possible. The usual noise of the breakfast trolley woke me at 8am the following morning. I had come to like it, to be honest.

The doctors always did their rounds each day at 11am. A member of my doctor's team arrived for a chat. He said that he couldn't believe the transformation in me, compared to the previous week, that all my statistics were really good, and that all going well, I may be allowed go home over the next few days. I joked with him that he was under pressure to get me home for the Late Late Toy Show.

Later on, just before dinner at 5pm, my kidney doctor, Dr. Declan deFreitas, popped into the ward for a chat. I was shocked and delighted by what he came to say to me,
'I'm going to allow you to go home!'

It was music to my ears, I honestly couldn't believe what I was hearing. I was so happy. He followed up that great news with,..

'Sure you might as well stay for your dinner!'

I was bursting with emotion. I immediately rang my family to tell them I was coming home. They were delighted. I got all my stuff together and waited on documentation that the hospital had to give to me. I ate my last dinner. It tasted nicer than any dinner I had eaten during my stay.

I have to give the nurses and healthcare staff a special mention, as they were amazing with the help and care that they showed me and the other patients during this pandemic. They work very long hours and they bravely step into work every day surrounded by infection and sickness, yet they are the kindest, most selfless, caring people on this Earth, so I would like to express a huge thank you to these amazing people.

I was advised to rest up by my doctor for two weeks when I got home and under no circumstances, engage in any exercise. My doctor knows me only too well that I would have jumped straight back into my training. I didn't honestly realise how badly my lungs would be affected post-Covid, so I heeded what he said and went home and enjoyed the rest. It had been the most horrendous few weeks of my life and I was glad for it to be over. I just wanted to be back to full health.

Amelia got her wish too. The Friday of that week, Amelia, Jennie and I bought treats, put on Christmas pyjamas, even though it was end of November, and we set ourselves up to watch the Late Late Toy Show. It was the first time Amelia ever stayed up to watch the whole. What a precious night it was for us all to be together again.

Home sweet home with my baby again. I think our smiles say it all.

One thing I learned from this horrible experience was that once again I had been faced with adversity and my mindset changed everything.

There were days when I felt so ill, I didn't shower or wash, and I just wasn't bothered with anything. I felt sorry for myself and had nearly given up. But when I received the card from my daughter, it just made me want to fight that bit harder. I knew sitting with her to watch the Late Late Toy Show would be my happy place.

No matter what you're going through, mentally, physically or emotionally, the only advice I can give you is to concentrate on the positive things in your life, things that brings you joy and make you happy, then channel any negative thoughts, if you can, into positive ones. It will help your mindset and in turn, make your situation more bearable, as no amount of worrying or stress will ever change the outcome of a situation.

Acknowledgements

As the saying goes, 'you can choose your friend but not your family'.

I feel extremely lucky to be in a position where I have the best friends and family in the world. It is an amazing feeling to have this in my life. Only for all these people combined, there were times and situations in my life that I may have not gotten through.

I have lost some people along the way through immaturity and childishness, but they were obviously not supposed to be in the final chapter of the story of my life, and that's ok with me. For the ones that are still there, I am so glad to have them. In this chapter I would like to pay special dedication to these people.

My wife, Jennie

I was very lucky to meet my wife Jennie later in my life, after I was over my transplant operation. When I met her, I instantly knew she was the one. I wanted to settle down with her and make my house a home. She was and still is a calming influence in my life, and we work as a great team in all aspects.

On December 29th, 2021, we celebrated 10 years of marriage, with very little ups and downs, great holidays,

Jennie and I enjoying dinner in our favourite restaurant.

fun times and a wonderful caring, intelligent, loving daughter, Amelia, together, including two new additions to the family, two shih tzu dogs, Ellie and Lulu.

Throughout the years and my super busy schedule, Jennie has been my rock, as patient as a saint, and I would like to express my love, thanks and admiration for her. I couldn't have done any of this without her.

My family, and my mother, Marie Kirwan

My family have been on this crazy journey from day one. They have always been so supportive. Thankfully, I didn't have many down days throughout it all and I stayed quite positive, but if I ever needed anything, they were there. I would like to especially thank my older brother, Niall, my older sister, Yvonne and my younger sister, Caitríona for all your support over the years. It's very much appreciated.

Left to right: My family – Niall, yvonne, mam, caitríona and myself

Like all other siblings, we have had our ups and downs, but I love you all dearly and always will.

In particular, I would like pay homage to my amazing mother, Marie Kirwan, who nursed me back to health after my operation. I rented out my own home in Ratoath for nearly two years and moved back home to my family home. I was supposed to stay off work for three months to recuperate, but I ended up going back to work after six weeks because I could not sit still.

While I was recuperating, my mam couldn't have done enough for me as she has done my whole life and still does to this day. She is an amazing woman, full of energy, with such a zest for life and an inspiration to all her children.

My fantastic mam; my inspiration in life.

My mam and Amelia at my mam's favourite restaurant

She is the glue that holds us all together and has many friends. She was so brave when my dad passed in 2006. We were so thankful that she had so many good friends at such a terrible time. Thank you Mam for being an amazing person.

My lifelong friends

Not many people keep their childhood friends right through to adulthood and heading for middle age, but I am very lucky to say that I have kept them right through.

We have been through thick and thin and have had great times along the way. We are all married or nearly married now with kids and are very successful in our lives and professions. I would also like to think that we have matured like fine wines.

Left to right: Brian, greg, brian, terry, myself and john

I have always been one of the wilder, crazy lads of the group, but I guess every group has to have one. My solid group of friends is a lot larger than this, but these lads are my constants for nearly 30 years now. I look forward to the next 30 years with them too.

All the staff at Beaumont Hospital and Dialysis Unit

I would like to express a special thank you to the staff at Beaumont Hospital and particularly, the staff in the Dialysis unit, since being diagnosed with my condition 21 years ago. I have received nothing but the best care and treatment.

Being faced with a condition such as polycystic kidney disease and the imminent possibility of dialysis was extremely daunting, but the nurses, doctors, and the healthcare assistants were the best in the world and looked after me so well. The dialysis sessions took place three nights a week for four hours a night, and the healthcare assistants were so caring and funny and made it all so bearable for me, which was a huge help.

To the nurses in Clinic C in the main part of Beaumont Hospital, who I still attend to this day, every three months for my check-ups, and to Claire who formerly worked in reception, there. They were and are brilliant. They had to listen to my whims, my questions, my peeves, etc, over the last many years, and they stayed very patient and helpful the whole time and still to this day, so thank you guys.

My professors in Beaumont Hospital
Professor Peter J Conlon & Dr. Declan deFreitas

Since I was diagnosed many years ago, these two men, Professor Peter J Conlon and Dr Declan deFreitas, have been instrumental in my health and welfare and the health of my kidney and still are to this day. I will admit that there were obviously times that I didn't like what they were telling me and I didn't want to hear it, but that was just my own ignorance.

To this day, I have lived a very healthy life since my transplant operation. There were a few hiccups along the way, but all in all, I have led a great, healthy life so far. They have done an amazing job in helping me achieve this.

I would like to express my sincere, heartfelt thanks to them both for keeping me and my transplanted organ healthy through the years. This is a condition I will have for life, I will be taking medication for life and my kidney may not last forever but that's life. I intend to live my life to the fullest every day and be happy.

Lightning Source UK Ltd.
Milton Keynes UK
UKHW020637150322
400092UK00009B/664